science by degrees

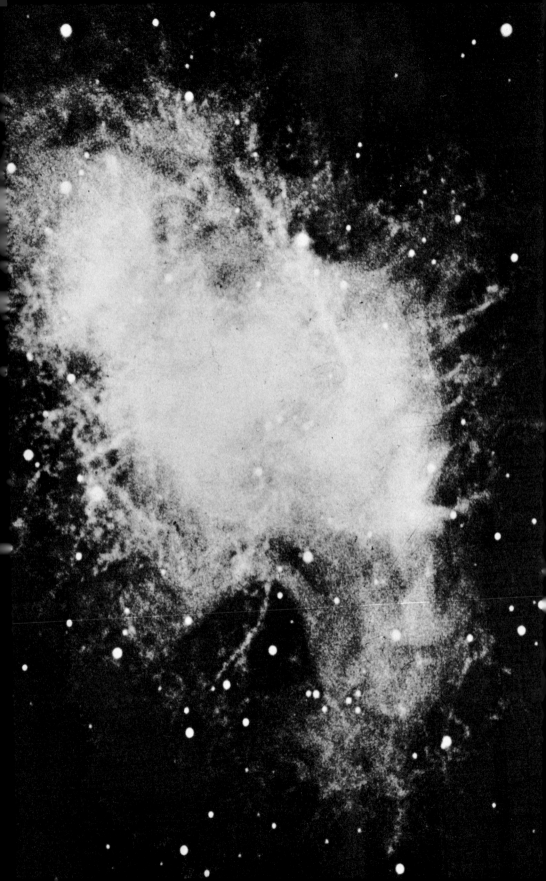

science
by degrees

TEMPERATURE FROM ZERO TO ZERO

by Scientists of the Westinghouse
Research Laboratories

JACK CASTLE, JR.
WERNER EMMERICH
ROBERT HEIKES
ROBERT MILLER
JOHN RAYNE
SHARON BANIGAN, *Executive Editor*

A Westinghouse Search Book

WALKER AND COMPANY

NEW YORK

Other Westinghouse Search Books

THE SCIENCE OF SCIENCE
ENERGY DOES MATTER
ELECTRONS ON THE MOVE

To the memory of

MILTON WACHTEL

whose tireless efforts, imagination, and enthusiasm guided the planning of this book, and whose untimely death has prevented his participation as an author.

Contents

APPENDIX

Foreword

TEMPERATURE is so much a part of everyday science—the happenings in the laboratory, in industry, in atomics, in the sun, the stars and space, in all living things and all creation—that the kind of precise, hard-won knowledge set forth in these pages is invaluable to the educated person. It is also essential to the millions of rising science students who are attempting to revolutionize our world year by year.

It has taken many years of experimental probing to get at the facts about temperature and heat. Heat was once thought to be a subtle, imponderable fluid that flowed from one object to another. There were countless discussions and controversies about this "caloric," as it was called. Count Rumford, one of the experimenters, made "An Experimental Inquiry Concerning the Source of Heat Which is Excited by Friction," and in 1798 he wrote:

> And, in reasoning on this subject, we must not forget to consider that most remarkable circumstance, that the source of the Heat generated by friction in these experiments, appeared evidently to be *inexhaustible*.
>
> It is hardly necessary to add that anything which any *insulated* body, or system of bodies, can continue to furnish *without limitation*, cannot possibly be a *material substance*; and it appears to me to be extremely difficult, if not quite impossible, to form any distinct idea of anything capable of being excited and communicated in the manner the Heat was excited and communicated in these experiments, except it be MOTION.

These were very modern conclusions for that time, and they predicted the way scientists think of heat today.

Foreword

Perhaps even closer to the material presented in *Science By Degrees* are the ideas of James Clerk Maxwell who, about a century after Count Rumford, stated in a classic textbook "Theory of Heat":

> Every hot body, therefore, is in motion. We have next to enquire into the nature of this motion. It is evidently not a motion of the whole body in one direction, for however small we make the body by mechanical processes, each visible particle remains apparently in the same place, however hot it is. The motion which we call heat must therefore be a motion of parts too small to be observed separately; the motions of different parts at the same instant must be in different directions; and the motion of any one part must, at least in solid bodies, be such that, however fast it moves, it never reaches a sensible distance from the point from which it started.

The present understanding and interpretation of temperature, heat, degrees, and so on—two centuries after Rumford and a century after Maxwell—is the subject of this book. The range of scientific experience has expanded to include not only temperatures just above absolute zero, but the immense temperatures of the sun and supernovae—temperatures measured in millions of degrees. Temperatures only a little above the coldest possible in theory can now be produced in many laboratories. The fourth state of matter—plasma—although still not commonplace, is beginning to be understood. It is also possible to attain the temperature at which electricity will flow—in some superconducting metals—almost forever. And it is now reasonable to contemplate a fifth state of matter.

With so much already known about temperature, the question may be: Is there a chance for more advances? This is always the query at the frontiers of knowledge. And always the answer is: Yes. So I feel justified in continuing the permissible pun of the title of this volume by saying that to an impressive degree this is very "hot stuff" indeed.

WATSON DAVIS
Director
Science Service

June 10, 1964

Introduction
Some Basic Ideas

A THERMOMETER is a familiar device—a simple, convenient, and apparently very accurate means of measuring temperature. What does this unique and universal label—the "temperature" of an object—actually signify?

Temperature is most obviously described by such words as "warm," "hot," "cool," and "cold." Indeed, it is well known that the human skin, as well as that of many animals, is endowed with sensory perceptors that are able to detect heat and cold. Simple experiments can be performed to map the temperature-sensitive areas of the skin, and it is found that nerve endings are very much localized, their density varying over different portions of the body. Also, the "hot" perceptors seem to be distinct from the "cold" ones.

With these senses, we can qualitatively evaluate the relative temperature of our surroundings. It seems apparent that additional temperature sensors must also be present for internal perception, because the temperature of the blood remains remarkably constant. We know that if the blood temperature varies more than a few degrees, either up or down, it is fatal to the human body.

Although plants and cold-blooded animals have much greater tolerance to temperature variations than human beings do, life on this planet exists only within the temperature range of the air on the earth's surface. In fact, life as we know it occurs only within the confines of a temperature span that represents less than one-billionth of the known temperature range. Outside these limits, we are mostly familiar in our daily lives with temperatures higher than those encountered in the weather, because of our long experience with fire. However, scientists have explored not only the high temperatures but lower ones as well. We will see later that there is an *absolute zero* below which temperature cannot go. A region of *negative* temperatures beyond infinite values can also be realized. In between, the temperature scale includes many interesting regions, as indicated in Fig. I.1.

Since temperature is a physical characteristic of matter, it is not surprising that physics, as a science, encompasses all regions shown in Fig. I.1. Conversely, temperature is a phenomenon that enters directly or indirectly into all areas of physics. It is closely related to energy, another interdisciplinary and fundamental concept in science. In fact, it may be worthwhile to investigate a few basic ideas about energy at this stage of our discussion to help clarify the meaning of temperature.

To begin with, let's take some simple object like a baseball. When hit with a bat, the ball acquires energy of motion, which is also called *kinetic* energy. Assuming that the ball does not rotate, its kinetic energy is proportional to the square of the velocity it has acquired. As long as the batter and all observers are standing still, there is no quarrel with the determination of the velocity. But suppose the baseball team is on tour, traveling in a train. The boys suddenly feel an urge to practice and start batting the ball around inside the railroad car. The question that now arises is whether the energy of the baseball should be measured using the velocity of the ball with respect to the moving train, or with respect to someone standing still in the station. The ball players are all inside the train, and the energy of the

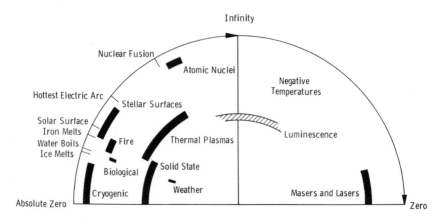

Figure I.1

ball as they see it is part of the train's *internal* energy. The additional energy, apparent only to the people outside the train, we shall call *external* energy.

This distinction becomes a little clearer if the internal energy is of a different kind than the external energy. For example, in a wrist watch, energy is imparted by the spring to a balance wheel. The rotational energy in the motion of this wheel is confined completely to the inside of the watch. This is *internal* kinetic energy of the watch, as opposed to any *external* kinetic energy the watch may have due to its motion as a whole with respect to its surroundings.

Let's take another example on a somewhat more grandiose scale. The earth, as a planet, has external kinetic energy due to its rotation and its motion around the sun. It also has internal kinetic energy that includes, among other things, all the objects moving on the earth's surface. Each one of these objects may, in turn, have external as well as internal energy. Molecules, for instance, execute vibrating and rotating motions even in solid materials, such as the baseball of the previous example. Each molecule, furthermore, contains atomic nuclei and electrons that are also in motion. The atomic nuclei are made up of protons and neutrons that move about inside. Thus, we not only have to differentiate between external and internal energy, but we also have to worry about many different kinds of internal kinetic energies. Fortunately, we can often ignore a number of these, so that the solution of a problem involving energy is not hopelessly complicated.

In summary, we can say that a physical object is usually composed of smaller objects, each of which can have a variety of internal and external energies, and that the external energies of the smaller objects are usually apparent as internal (heat) energy of the larger object. This internal energy of the gross object is related to its external characteristic called temperature.

The useful concept of a *particle* has been implied in the preceding discussion. Any physical object behaves like a particle when its internal energy remains constant. Therefore, we will often find that the smaller objects which make up a gross object behave as particles over a reasonable temperature range.

Before going on with temperature, we should mention another point about energy. A complete accounting of the energy in any series of events must show the total to be conserved. Hence, in the ball game, as the ball is hit straight up it slows down (losing kinetic energy), stops momentarily (zero kinetic energy), and then regains its original kinetic energy just before landing in the catcher's mitt. We picture the conservation of the ball's energy for the period after it is hit and before it lands as the trading of kinetic energy for energy of position in the earth's gravitational field. This is called *potential* energy. The word potential connotes the idea of energy that is stored and kept available for reconversion to energy of motion.

Such an exchange between kinetic and potential energy is a very common phenomenon observed not only in the gravitation of the earth, but wherever forces occur that are associated with an elastic medium. Springs, air cushions, electric and magnetic fields, and many others are essentially in this category. In molecular and atomic physics, too, we encounter potential energy due to forces operating within the material. In analogy to the baseball, the energy of each molecular or atomic particle may be partially potential and partially kinetic.

Being fond of pictures, the scientist draws a diagram to show schematically the energy values possible for a single particle, arranged vertically as in Fig. I.2. If he has determined the energy of the particle, he will locate it in the corresponding vertical position or level, as shown. He says that the particle "occupies that *energy level*." As we will see shortly, temperature can usually be related to the manner in which particles occupy energy levels.

Kinetic, potential, internal, and external are not the only labels scientists give energy. Energy is also commonly described by the manner in which it manifests itself. We have mechanical, electrical, chemical, and nuclear energy, as well as light, heat, sound, and radiation. All are manifestations of energy. It is unnecessary to discuss these forms here, but we must keep in mind that when they are mentioned in connection with an object or a medium, they can all be classified as kinetic or potential, internal or external energy of that particular object or medium.

Let's now continue with the concept of temperature which was initially introduced from the point of view of the human senses. It can be readily appreciated that we can make little scientific or engineering use of temperature unless we can find a way to define it more precisely and, in addition, formulate a means for its accurate measurement. Our own senses do not provide any objective means for comparing the

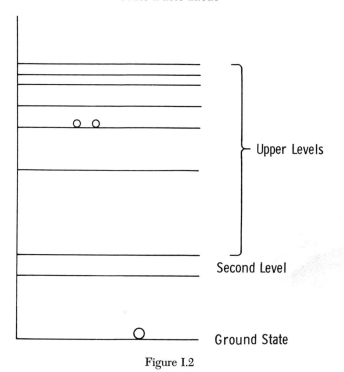

Figure I.2

temperature of two objects. There will be little correspondence between the temperature claimed by different observers, since their senses certainly do not possess the same degree of sensitivity.

In order to lay the proper groundwork for understanding temperature, we need first to take a good look at the world around us. Any object—solid, liquid, or gas—can be regarded on two different scales. The more familiar is the *macroscopic* scale, the less familiar is the *microscopic*. Let's discuss the macroscopic first, using a container filled with a gas as an example. Suppose our task is to determine the characteristic features (usually called *parameters*) of this gas, including the particular conditions under which it exists in the container. First, we want to know its *chemical composition*. Let's assume that in this example the gas is helium, He. Of course, it might have been oxygen, hydrogen, nitrogen, or any one of a number of others—or even a mixture of two or more. In any event, the gross composition is certainly one convenient macroscopic parameter, and another is the *volume* the gas occupies. A third parameter is the *pressure* the gas exerts on the walls of the container, and a fourth parameter is the *temperature* of the gas. If we were to determine all of these parameters, we would have a reasonably complete identification of this particular gas sample. We would have the composition, the volume, the pressure, and the temperature, which gives us a description in terms of macroscopic parameters. This type of description consists of measuring a few, easily obtainable gross properties. It should be noted that we needed to make no assumption about the internal structure of the gas itself.

Now, suppose we examine the same container of gas on a much finer scale—the microscopic scale. We know that a gas is composed of great numbers of atoms. In fact, a cubic centimeter of gas at atmospheric pressure and room temperature contains approximately 10^{20} atoms—and these atoms are not at rest. In the case of helium, they are moving with an average speed of about 15×10^4 cm/sec, as we will see later. We also know that, because of collisions with other atoms and with the walls of the container, the velocity (which refers to both speed and direction) is changing rapidly. How do we describe the gas on a microscopic scale?

It is obviously impossible to follow the motion of each individual gas atom as it goes chaotically about its business, because this would mean keeping track of some 10^{20} atoms simply to describe one cubic centimeter of gas. Since at room temperature and atmospheric pressure each gas atom makes an average of 10^9 collisions per second, it is obviously impractical to try to follow individual atoms. Furthermore, even if we were able to describe perfectly the motion of a given atom over a period of one second on a single sheet of paper one-thousandth of an inch thick, it would take an enormously thick book to describe the whole volume of gas for even one second. In fact, such a book would just barely fit between here and the nearest star. Therefore, we use a different kind of description.

Let's suppose that at a given instant of time, we can measure the kinetic energy of each particle, remembering that kinetic energy is equal to $\frac{1}{2}$ mass times (velocity)^2. We would then be able to say that a number n_1 of the particles has an energy between zero and E_1, a number n_2 has an energy between E_1 and E_2, and so on. Thus, we would know the total number of helium atoms in the container and their total kinetic energy. We would also have a knowledge of the way in which the energy is distributed among the particles. It will turn out that this information gives us a sufficiently complete description of the microscopic systems to allow us to evaluate all desired macroscopic properties.

Now let's recapitulate. Of these two descriptions of the container of helium gas, the first—the macroscopic—consists of measuring a few, easily obtainable gross properties. We need to make no special assumptions about the structure of the gas. In the case of the second description—the microscopic one—we must make some assumptions about the composition of the body. We assume, for instance, the existence of helium atoms in our example. Furthermore, many quantities must be specified, quantities not normally suggested by our sense perceptions. Finally, these quantities cannot be measured directly. We have no direct way of measuring the energy of each gas atom, for example.

It is important to realize that the macroscopic properties, those easily available to our sense perceptions, *must* come about as a direct result of the microscopic properties. One of our objectives is to relate the measured temperature, a macroscopic parameter, to the microscopic properties of a body. But before we attempt to do this, let's consider a somewhat simpler problem: the pressure. Suppose we have a box of side L, as shown in Fig. I.3, containing a gas. The force per unit area exerted by the gas on the walls of this container is termed the *pressure*. We want to calculate the pressure, a macroscopic quantity, on a microscopic model.

We assume all N atoms have a mass m and a velocity of magnitude v. (Although we will see later that the assumption of a single speed is not correct, it will be simpler to overlook this point now.) It is reasonable to assume that the directions in which the particles move are completely random. (The speeds are fixed by our previous assumption, while an equal number of particles will be traveling in any arbitrary direction.) To simplify the mathematics, we make the further, very unrealistic assumption that the particles can travel only along the x, y, and z axes. This means that we will have $\frac{N}{3}$ atoms traveling along each of the axes.

What happens when an atom collides with the side of the container? Assume that just before collision with the wall, the velocity of the particle is $+v$. Just after collision, the velocity is $-v$. Clearly, the

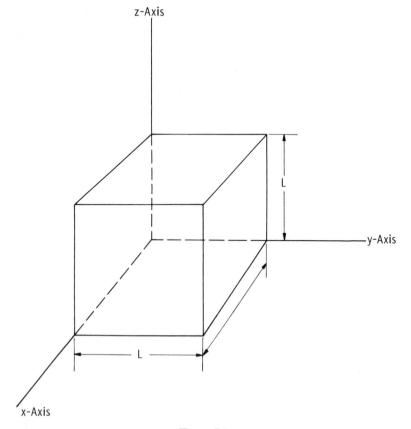

Figure I.3

atom has exerted a force on the wall by this collision. We will now show that the force exerted by all the atoms striking a container wall is just equal to the pressure.

Newton's second law states that

$$F = ma, \tag{I.1}$$

where F is the force, m the mass, and a the acceleration. Remembering that a is the change in velocity in a given time, we can write

$$a = \frac{v_2 - v_1}{t_2 - t_1} = \frac{\Delta v}{\Delta t}, \tag{I.2}$$

where v_1 is the velocity at time t_1, and v_2 is the velocity at a later time t_2.

Now, from Newton's law of action and reaction, we know that the wall must exert a force on the atom that is equal and opposite to the force the atom exerts on the wall. Since the force from the wall causes the atom's velocity to change from $+v$ to $-v$, we see from Eqs. I.1 and I.2 that

$$\overline{F} = \frac{m\Delta v}{\Delta t} = \frac{2mv}{\Delta t}, \tag{I.3}$$

where Δt is the time of contact with the wall, and $\overline{F}$ is the average force exerted during the time Δt. This equation is more instructive if we write it

$$\overline{F}\Delta t = 2mv. \tag{I.4}$$

$F\Delta t$ is termed the *impulse*. On a macroscopic scale, of course, we cannot tell just when the particle collides with the wall or, for that matter, the exact duration of the contact. However, we can make a diagram, such as Fig. I.4, showing what happens on collision. The force between the particle and the wall builds up from zero to some maximum value, and then goes back to zero. The accompanying high-speed photograph of a tennis ball hitting a plate illustrates this idea. The amount of the ball's deformation is, of course, a measure of the force exerted on the ball by the plate.

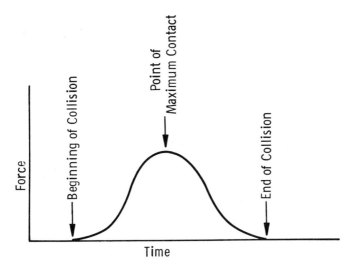

Figure I.4

Microflash photograph showing how a tennis ball is deformed when striking a rigid surface. Gas atoms behave in a similar manner when colliding with the wall of a container, as described in the text.

Now let's calculate the total impulse that a wall perpendicular to the x axis receives from all the atoms in one second of time. We see that

$$\text{Total impulse/sec} = (2mv) \times (\text{number of particles moving along } x \text{ axis}) \times (\text{number of wall collisions per second}). \quad \text{(I.5)}$$

We have already seen that the number of particles moving along the x axis is $\dfrac{N}{3}$. The number of collisions for each particle per second is easily seen to be $\dfrac{v}{2L}$, the factor of 2 indicating that only one half of the collisions are with the wall in question. Thus,

$$\text{Total impulse/sec} = 2mv \times \frac{N}{3} \times \frac{v}{2L}. \quad \text{(I.6)}$$

This total impulse is simply equal to the average total force F_T on the wall multiplied by the length of time this force is applied. Thus,

$$\text{Total impulse} = F_T \times (1 \text{ second}),$$

and therefore we have

$$F_T = (\text{total impulse})/(1 \text{ second}).$$

In other words, Eq. I.6 gives the total force on the wall. If we now divide both sides by L^2, the area of the wall, on the left side we have the force per unit area. This equals the pressure. Thus, we write the pressure, denoted by P, as follows:

$$P = \frac{2}{3} \frac{N}{L^3} \frac{1}{2} mv^2 = \frac{2}{3} n(\text{KE}), \tag{I.7}$$

where KE is the external kinetic energy of a particle, and n is the number of particles per unit volume. We see that the concept of pressure is simply related to the total kinetic energy of the gas atoms.

What about the simplification we introduced at the beginning of this problem? We assumed that all the gas atoms had equal speeds, although we have already guessed that this is obviously not so. Furthermore, we made the calculation of the pressure of a model that allowed atoms to be traveling only along three coordinate axes. Unfortunately, without these two simplifying assumptions, the calculation is rather complicated mathematically; however, it can be done, and the result of Eq. I.7 is found to be a general one.

PART 1

View from the Outside

The Macroscopic
Picture

ANY DISCUSSION of temperature has to rely on some understanding of *equilibrium*. We describe a substance as being in equilibrium if its macroscopic properties are not dependent on time. As an example, suppose we were to take a block of copper from boiling water and drop it into ice water. The system composed of water plus copper block is not in equilibrium, because the macroscopic properties of both water and copper are changing with time. However, after a sufficient length of time, we know that the macroscopic properties will vary so very slowly with the passing of time that to some specified accuracy they will be independent of time. In this condition, the several parts are said (to that accuracy) to have reached equilibrium.

What do we mean by "a sufficient length of time"? Actually there is no simple answer to this question. Let's consider two extreme examples. In Fig. 1.1a we have a box with a partition dividing it in half. The left side is filled with gas A at atmospheric pressure, and the right side is filled with gas B at the same pressure. We now remove the partition. If the dimensions of this box are as indicated, equilibrium will be obtained within a matter of minutes after the partition is removed. In other words, gases A and B will be homogeneously distributed throughout the total volume. On the other hand, consider the

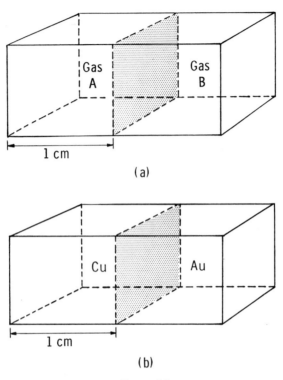

Figure 1.1

situation in Fig. 1.1b. Here we have a cubic centimeter of gold in contact with a cubic centimeter of copper. For the two metals to reach equilibrium—that is, for a homogeneous crystalline solid solution to be formed—it would take about a million years at room temperature. Obviously, the length of time necessary to achieve equilibrium can range over wide limits.

Pursuing the concept of equilibrium a little further, let's consider two types of contacts that may occur between macroscopic systems. The first is a *thermal* contact, and the second is an *adiabatic* contact. To illustrate these terms, let's suppose we have a copper container filled with cold water, as shown in Fig. 1.2, and we lower this into a larger container of boiling water. We know from experience that the water in the inner container will soon begin to boil. This is evidence of the fact that heat passes through the walls of the copper container into the water. The copper separating the hot and cold water is a thermal contact, one that allows heat to pass. In contrast, an adiabatic contact is one that does *not* allow heat to pass. It is obvious that an adiabatic contact is an idealization that cannot exist in reality. All known substances allow some heat to pass through them. If this were not so, problems of thermal insulation would be much less troublesome.

In the light of these ideas, let's consider Fig. 1.3. Since systems A and C are in thermal contact, they will eventually reach an equilibrium. Systems B and C, being in thermal contact, will eventually also reach equilibrium. However, systems A and B are separated by an adiabatic contact. If now the adiabatic contact between A and B is

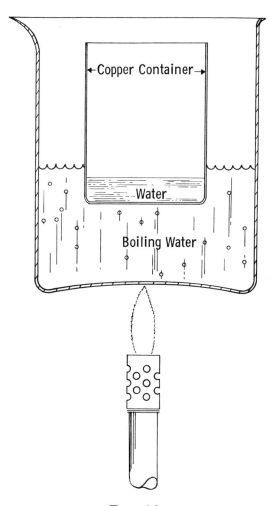

Figure 1.2

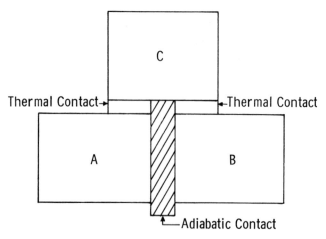

Figure 1.3

replaced by a thermal contact, no further changes are observed in the systems. By our definition of equilibrium, this most certainly means that A and B were in equilibrium without actually having been in direct thermal contact. The obvious conclusion is that if two systems are in equilibrium with a third system, they must be in equilibrium with each other. This is sometimes referred to as the *zeroth law of thermodynamics*, and it is very important in defining the concept of temperature.

WHAT DOES TEMPERATURE MEAN?[*]

We are now ready to describe temperature itself. First, let's consider a large volume of gas, the reference system, at some pressure P_0' and volume V_0', as indicated in Fig. 1.4. We bring into thermal contact with this reference system a small vessel, the test system, of volume V_1', containing a fixed quantity of gas. The relative sizes of these systems are important; the reference system must be large enough so that its state will not be changed by thermal contact with the test system. For example, if the test system were an ice cube dropped into a glass of hot water—the reference system—the temperature of the reference system obviously would have changed appre-

[*] The introduction of the concept of temperature is patterned after that of M. Zemansky in *Heat and Thermodynamics*.

ciably at equilibrium. However, if the reference system were a swimming pool of hot water, adding the ice cube would not cause a detectable change.

When the two gas systems are allowed to come to thermal equilibrium, we find a pressure P_1' is needed to maintain the test system at a volume V_1'. If we now remove the test system, alter its volume to V_2', say, and again bring it into thermal contact with the reference system, a pressure P_2' will be found when equilibrium is reached. In the same manner, a whole series of equilibrium states of the test system can be found that are in equilibrium with the reference system at pressure P_0' and volume V_0'. According to the zeroth law, each of the states (P_1', V_1'), (P_2', V_2'), (P_3', V_3'), and so on, must all be in equilibrium with each other and with the state (P_0', V_0'). If we now change the state of the reference system by making its pressure P_0'' and its volume V_0'', we find a whole new set of states of the test system (P_1'', V_1''), (P_2'', V_2''), and so forth, which are in equilibrium with the reference system and thereby with each other.

We may represent this graphically, as in Fig. 1.5. On the graph of pressure versus volume, we plot the coordinates—the pressure and the volume—of all the states that are in equilibrium with the first state (I) of the reference system. Then we plot the coordinates in all the states that are in equilibrium with the second state (II) of the reference system. We now draw a smooth line through the coordinates. We can see that every possible state on curve I (each of these curves is called

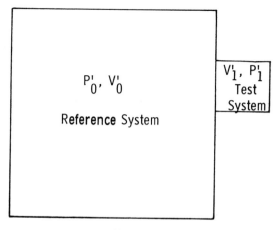

Figure 1.4

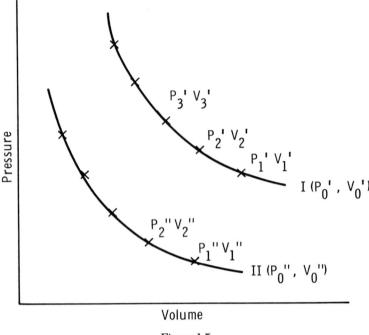

Figure 1.5

an *isotherm*) is in equilibrium with state I (P_0', V_0') of the reference system. This means that all states of the test system on curve I have a property in common with the reference system; that is, the various states possess a property that insures their being in thermal equilibrium with each other. We call this property *temperature*.

Now, the temperature of all systems in thermal equilibrium may be represented by a number—the same number. Establishing a temperature scale is merely adopting a set of rules for the assignment of one number to one isotherm, and a different number to a different isotherm. Once this is done, the condition for thermal equilibrium is simply that they have the same temperature. Conversely, when the temperatures are different, we may be sure that the systems are not in thermal equilibrium.

SETTING UP A TEMPERATURE SCALE

We are now ready to assign numbers to the isotherms; that is, we are going to set up a temperature scale. In Fig. 1.6, the isotherm labeled *ice* is formed from the set of pressures and volumes determined from a reference system in equilibrium with a mixture of ice and water. The isotherm labeled *steam* is similarly formed. These two particular isotherms have been singled out in the following treatment only for convenience; any other set of reference points would be just as sound on a technical basis. A number is now assigned to each of these isotherms. Assuming for the moment that we have done this, we may then measure the temperature of an object by placing a test system (a thermometer) in contact with the object whose temperature we want to know. When equilibrium is attained, we measure the P and V of the test system and then look at our chart. For example, if $V = 10$ and $P = 4$, we find the temperature, $T = A$. It is probably clear that such a procedure is unnecessarily complicated. Therefore, let's choose instead a standard volume V_T for our thermometer, and then we need to worry only about pressure. In other words, we need measure only the pressure in the thermometer, rather than both pressure and volume.

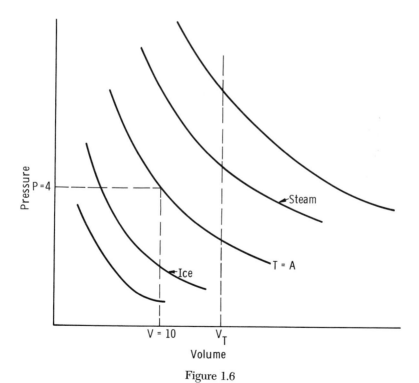

Figure 1.6

Setting up the actual temperature scale involves assigning a number (the temperature) to each value of the pressure of our thermometer. This assignment can be almost completely arbitrary. The only restriction is that the assigned sequence of numbers must either increase or decrease continuously with increasing pressure. This restriction is necessary so that the relation between pressure and temperature is unique. The kind of difficulty that might otherwise be found is illustrated in Fig. 1.7. Because the temperature does not increase continuously with the pressure, we see that we have two different pressures represented by the same temperature. From our definition of temperature, we know that this is not possible, because the systems at pressures P_1 and P_2 could not be in equilibrium, and therefore could not have the same temperature.

One of the simpler possibilities for actually assigning a system of numbers to the isotherms is illustrated in Fig. 1.8. We may assign a number A to the ice isotherm, and a number B to the steam isotherm. It is then reasonable to simply draw a straight line through these two points, as shown in Fig. 1.8. This is only a choice of convenience and has no physical significance. Now, such a straight line can always be represented by an equation of the form

$$t = aP + b, \tag{1.1}$$

where t is the temperature and P is the pressure; a and b are constants to be determined so that the straight line passes through the designated

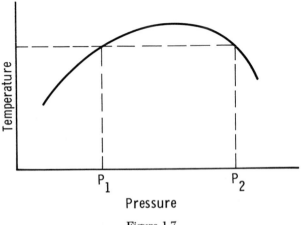

Figure 1.7

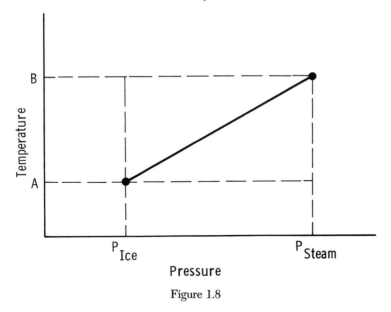

Figure 1.8

points. If we now choose to assign the number 0 to the ice isotherm and the number 100 to the steam isotherm, we have two simultaneous equations to determine a and b:

$$0 = aP_i + b,$$
$$100 = aP_s + b,$$

where P_i is the pressure of our test system at ice temperature, and P_s is the pressure of our test system at steam temperature. If we solve these two equations simultaneously, we find

$$a = \frac{100}{P_s - P_i}, \tag{1.2}$$

$$b = \frac{100\,P_i}{P_s - P_i}. \tag{1.3}$$

Thus,

$$t = 100\,\frac{P - P_i}{P_s - P_i}. \tag{1.4}$$

Let's see what this equation means. If we bring our thermometer (test system) into contact with some object whose temperature we want to know, we must first allow it to come to equilibrium with the object.

We then measure the pressure P in the thermometer. From the above equation, we may determine the temperature t. (It is worthwhile to consider once again the importance of the relationship between the volume of the thermometer and the volume of the system to be measured. We must be concerned with the same problem we met in setting up the temperature scale originally. There we wanted the reference system large compared to the test system.)

We might, of course, build thermometers using other physical properties. For example, we might use the fact that the resistance R of a platinum wire varies with temperature. If we assume that

$$t = aR + b, \tag{1.5}$$

a temperature scale can be set up as above. Also, we can use as the thermometric property the thermal expansion of a metal or a liquid, such as mercury. The common household thermometer is of this latter type.

Now we want to know how the various thermometers will agree with one another. We might ask, "Why shouldn't they agree?" Well, we have seen that our temperature scales have been set up on such a basis that the temperature is dependent on the *first* power of the thermometric property. In the case of the constant-volume gas thermometer, we defined a temperature scale in terms of the pressure of the gas (and not the square or the cube of the pressure). In the case of the platinum resistance thermometer, we again defined a temperature in terms of the resistance of the platinum (and not the square or the cube of the resistance). A little thought will reveal that it would be quite a coincidence if the two scales were identical. So far as the platinum wire is concerned, the temperature scale set up from the constant-volume gas thermometer is completely arbitrary. Therefore, it would be quite fortuitous if the resistance of the platinum wire depended on the first power of the arbitrary temperature scale set up from the constant-volume gas thermometer.

Let's now pursue the question more quantitatively. Assume that we have available a number of different thermometers—constant-volume gas thermometers (we will use several containing different gases), a platinum resistance thermometer, and a mercury thermometer. Let's take a constant-volume hydrogen thermometer as the standard and measure a set of objects whose temperature (as measured by the hydrogen thermometer) varies from 0 to 100. Since the points 0 and 100 are set, all thermometers will read the same at these points. However, at intermediate points there will be a variance as shown in Table 1.A. We can see that the two constant-volume gas thermometers are in best agreement. Furthermore, this is generally found to be the case; that is, the smallest variation is found among different gas thermometers. For this reason, gas is chosen as the standard thermometric substance. Extensive experiments have shown that as the gas pressure in the various gas thermometers is lowered, the difference in indicated temperature becomes less. This fact gives us a rigorous definition of the Celsius (centigrade) scale. We may write

$$t = \left\{ 100 \frac{P - P_i}{P_s - P_i} \right\}_{P_i \to 0} \tag{1.6}$$

This equation means that the centigrade temperature scale is obtained with a constant-volume gas thermometer in which the gas pressure is allowed to go toward zero. The same group of experiments that lead to the above scale also show that the quantity $P_i/(P_s - P_i)$ is the same for all gases as P_i goes to zero; that is, it is a universal constant as P_i goes to zero. Thus, we may rewrite the centigrade scale as

$$t = 100 \frac{P}{P_s - P_i} - 100 \frac{P_i}{P_s - P_i}, \tag{1.7}$$

TABLE 1.A*

Comparison of Thermometers

Constant-volume hydrogen thermometer	Constant-volume air thermometer	Platinum-resistance thermometer	Mercury thermometer
$t(P)$	$t(P)$	$t(R)$	$t(L)$
0	0	0	0
20	20.008	20.240	20.091
40	40.001	40.360	40.111
60	59.990	60.360	60.086
80	79.987	80.240	80.041
100	100	100	100

* Table 1.A abstracted from M. Zemansky, *Heat and Thermodynamics.*

where the second term is constant. Let's call it I. We now define an *absolute* temperature scale as

$$T = t + I = 100 \frac{P}{P_s - P_i}. \qquad (1.8)$$

It is found experimentally that $I = -273.16°$ C. The quantity $t + I$ is called the absolute temperature, and we see that the absolute temperature scale is directly related to the pressure of a constant-volume gas thermometer. We will discuss the absolute temperature scale in more detail later.

TEMPERATURE AND HEAT

Now that we have some understanding of the basic meaning of temperature from the macroscopic point of view, we are prepared to pursue the thermal properties of matter a bit further. How much heat must be supplied to a substance in order to alter its temperature from, say, T_1 to T_2? To answer this question, we need to introduce a quantity called the *heat capacity*.

Let's suppose we place two beakers on a hot plate. In one beaker we put a block of aluminum, and in the other an equal *weight* of water. If we observe the temperature of the water and the aluminum after the hot plate is turned on, we notice that the temperature of the aluminum rises much faster than that of the water. This is a result of the fact that the heat capacity of the aluminum is smaller than that of the water. The heat capacity is essentially a measure of the amount of heat an object must absorb in order to increase its temperature by a prescribed amount. Usually, the definition is in terms of the amount of heat required to raise the temperature of one gram of material by 1°C. In general, we may write

$$Q = C\Delta T, \qquad (1.9)$$

where Q is the heat added to the substance, C is the heat capacity, and ΔT is the change in temperature. It should be mentioned immediately that C varies with the temperature, and it is therefore necessary to be careful about the temperature range over which Eq. 1.9 is used.

Obviously, the heat capacity C is a very important property of matter, and we would now like to calculate it from our knowledge of the macroscopic properties of matter. Consider a vessel containing a liquid with a piston of a given weight resting on top of it, as shown schematically in Fig. 1.9. What happens (macroscopically) if heat is added to the liquid? (Let's assume that the container is so thin that it does not contribute to the heat capacity.) This heat may be added by simply bringing the vessel into contact with another body at a higher temperature. Two things will happen. First, the temperature of the liquid will increase; second, the liquid will expand, raising the piston. The Law of Conservation of Energy states that energy cannot be created or destroyed—only converted from one form to another. Now consider the various forms of energy with which we are dealing in the above experiment. The heat added from the external source is the total energy added to the system. This energy shows itself in two ways: First, the liquid expands and raises the piston. If the piston has a weight w and is moved a distance χ, the work W done by the water

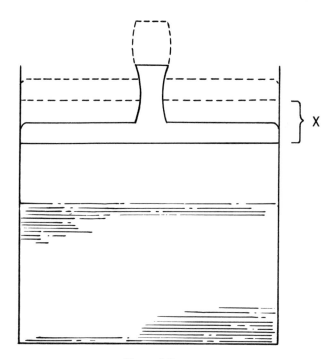

Figure 1.9

is $W = wx$. Second, the remainder of the energy goes into increasing the temperature of the liquid. Thus, we may write

$$Q = \Delta E + W. \tag{1.10}$$

In other words, the heat added Q shows up in the form of doing a certain amount of work W and increasing the energy of the liquid by an amount ΔE. Now it becomes apparent how to calculate the heat capacity. From Eqs. 1.9 and 1.10, we have

$$Q = E + W = C\Delta T. \tag{1.11}$$

Thus,

$$C = \frac{\Delta E}{\Delta T} + \frac{W}{\Delta T}. \tag{1.12}$$

This expression raises an important point. Suppose instead of having a movable piston, we fixed the piston so that it could not move. Clearly, the work W would then equal zero. Thus,

$$C = \frac{\Delta E}{\Delta T}. \tag{1.13}$$

We see that the heat capacity C depends on the conditions of measurement. In the case of Eq. 1.12, we refer to C_p, heat capacity at constant pressure, while in Eq. 1.13, we refer to C_v, heat capacity at constant volume. Since almost all substances expand when heated, we see that C_p is normally larger than C_v. Thus, the heat capacity (at constant volume) is simply the change in energy ΔE of the system when the system undergoes a change in temperature ΔT. Later, when we investigate the microscopic scale, we will deal with C_v because it is simpler. Actually, this is about as far as we can go with the macroscopic picture. We are able to infer the existence of energy, but we have no way of calculating it.

Finally, it becomes apparent that Eqs. 1.12 and 1.13 are true not only for liquids but for any state of matter.

Solid, Liquid, or Gas?

TEMPERATURE does not exist except as a property of a material body. Therefore, the phrase "effect of temperature," although convenient, is not strictly correct. What we really mean is the change that takes place in a material when it is heated or cooled and its temperature changes.

Of the many interesting effects observed with a change in temperature, one of the most spectacular is a phenomenon called *change of state*. This means that a material in a particular *state of aggregation* changes to a different state; a solid melts to a liquid, for example, as its temperature is increased.

Let's first consider the properties of several real substances. Everyone is acquainted with water in three states of aggregation—solid, liquid, and gas. In fact, these forms are so commonly encountered in our everyday lives that we refer to them by different names—ice, water, and steam. Perhaps a less familiar fact is that *any* substance, under the proper conditions of temperature and pressure, can be made to exist in any one of these three states. Of course, the conditions vary with the given substance or material. As two extreme examples, gaseous helium must be cooled below $-268°C$ before it will liquefy, and solid carbon must be heated to over $3500°C$ before it will melt. Some substances are able to exist not only in the three states of aggregation but also in several different forms in a given state. For example, solid carbon can be either diamond, one of the hardest substances known, or graphite, a black flaky material used as a lubricant and in pencil leads. Another example is ice; there are at least six different kinds of ice, each having a slightly different crystal structure. These forms of a given material are referred to as *phases*. More exactly defined, a phase is a homogeneous mass of material separated from its surroundings by distinct boundaries.

A glass of water serves as an example. The water is homogeneous and surrounded by distinct boundaries, glass on the sides and bottom, air on the top. The water is a phase. Similarly, a block of ordinary ice is a phase, and so is the steam in a boiler. Furthermore, a distinct mass of any of the other forms of ice is a phase, under conditions of temperature and pressure that allow the ice to be stable. Thus, in a water system there are at least eight possible phases—six solid, one liquid, and one gaseous—although there are only three states of aggregation —solid, liquid, and gas.

In the following discussion, we will refer most frequently to *argon*, which under normal conditions of temperature and pressure is a gas. Argon is a very common material in that it constitutes by weight 1.7 percent of our atmosphere. In fact, each square mile of the earth's surface supports 800,000 pounds of argon. Chemically inert, argon does not form any compounds. Because it is inert and structurally simple, its properties have been investigated extensively. The accumulated data on argon and a few other simple materials, which we will use here, have aided in the development of theories of atomic and molecular structure.

What are the conditions of temperature and pressure that determine if the various phases of a given substance are stable? Because this information is of great technical importance, the stability range of various phases has been determined for many substances. Often such information is illustrated in a phase diagram, such as that for argon in Figs. 2.1, 2.2, and 2.3. These figures are identical except for the pressure scales, which have been expanded to show some of the detail. In these diagrams and all others we will use, the pressure is expressed in *atmospheres*. An atmosphere is the pressure exerted on an object by the weight of the air above it. Since this pressure varies with the

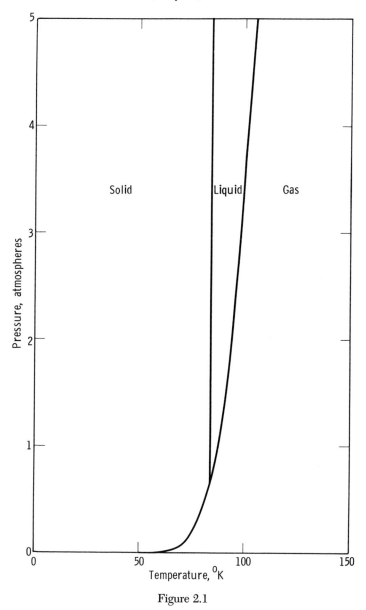

Figure 2.1

object's height above sea level and also with weather conditions, a standard atmosphere is defined as equal to 14.696 pounds per square inch, or 1.0333 kilograms per cm².

Principally because it is chemically inert, argon has the simplest kind of phase diagram observed for any real substance. If we examine

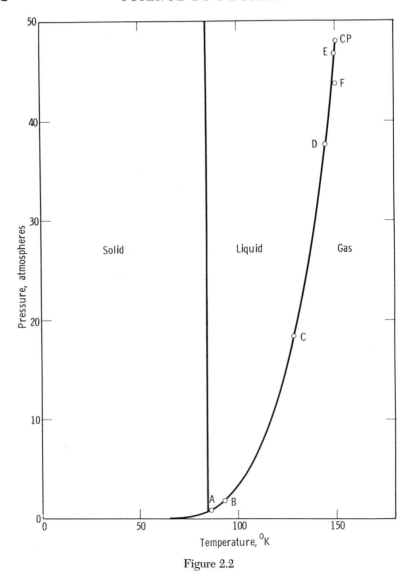

Figure 2.2

Fig. 2.1, we see that the diagram is divided into three regions—solid, liquid, and gas. A mass of argon at a temperature and pressure corresponding to a point inside one of these regions will be completely solid, or liquid, or gas, depending on the particular region in which the point lies. If the temperature and pressure of the argon corresponds to a point on one of the lines dividing two regions, this indicates the possibility of having two phases present simultaneously.

At the *triple point*, where three lines meet, there is the possibility of having all the phases present.

Three simple experiments will be helpful in showing how data are obtained to construct a phase diagram, and also in demonstrating the significance of the lines and points at which two or more phases are present simultaneously.

First, let's consider what happens when we cool a fixed mass of argon gas while maintaining it at constant pressure. The apparatus for

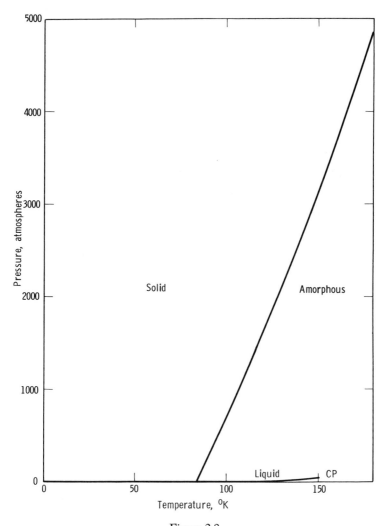

Figure 2.3

this experiment must maintain the argon at constant pressure, regardless of changes in temperature and volume. Such a device, shown in Fig. 2.4, consists of a cylinder with a frictionless piston, free to slide, and a weight or some means of exerting constant force on the piston. If the space is completely filled with argon, the pressure is simply the total force divided by the area of the piston. The volume of the argon is the piston's area multiplied by its distance above the bottom of the cylinder. Thus, as long as the force on the piston is constant, the pressure on the argon will be independent of its volume; furthermore, if the dimensions of the cylinder and piston do not change with temperature, the pressure is independent of the temperature.

To start, we place one mole (39.944 grams) of argon in this apparatus and adjust the temperature to 100°K and the pressure to one atmosphere. Since the weight of the air acting on the piston is sufficient to give one atmosphere of pressure, it is not necessary to add any more weight to the piston; in fact, we have to assume that the piston itself is weightless in order to obtain the desired pressure of one atmosphere. By referring to the phase diagram, we see that the temperature and pressure of the argon correspond to a point in the gaseous region. Under these conditions, the volume of one mole of argon gas is roughly 8000 cc. Now, if we remove a small amount of heat q from

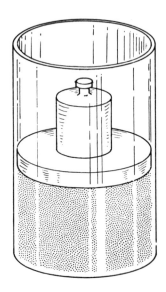

Figure 2.4

the apparatus and wait long enough to establish thermal equilibrium, we find the temperature and volume of the argon have decreased. The change in temperature ΔT and the amount of heat removed are related by the equation

$$\Delta T = \frac{q}{C_p},$$

where the quantity C_p is the heat capacity at constant pressure. In a real experiment additional heat would have to be removed from the apparatus itself. Furthermore, heat would leak into the apparatus from the surroundings. It is normally a simple problem to correct for these difficulties in the laboratory.

For our purposes, let's assume the container has zero heat capacity and that no heat is received from the surroundings. (Since we are dealing with a hypothetical apparatus, we call it a *system* to distinguish it from a real device.) If we continue to remove small amounts of heat from the system, and note its temperature and volume when thermal equilibrium is established after each succeeding removal of heat, we obtain the data necessary to construct Fig. 2.5 and Fig. 2.6. The vertical scale Q in Fig. 2.5 is the total amount of heat removed in changing the temperature of one mole of argon from 100°K to the temperature T. In other words, Q is simply the sum of individual increments q of heat removed. We notice that the temperature decreases smoothly as heat is removed, until the argon reaches a temperature of 87.4°K. At this temperature, which corresponds to the boundary between the gaseous and liquid regions at one atmosphere, a large amount of heat must be removed before there is any further change in temperature.

If we examine the argon when it first reaches 87.4°K, we observe that it is completely gaseous. As further heat is removed, there is no change in temperature and a few droplets of liquid are formed. As still more heat is removed, the volume of liquid increases and the volume of gas decreases, until the argon is completely liquid. After this point, further removal of heat causes the temperature to drop. If we reverse the procedure and add heat to liquid argon at 87.4°K, the liquid is converted into gas, and we see that this temperature corresponds to the boiling point at one atmosphere. Other points along the line separating the liquid and gaseous regions give the boiling points at various pressures. This line is called the *boiling point curve*. The amount of

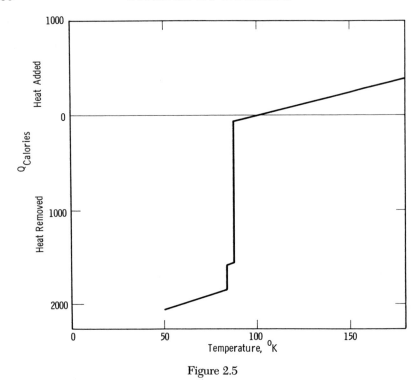

Figure 2.5

heat required to convert one mole of liquid at the boiling point to gas at the boiling point is called the *latent heat of vaporization.*

At this boundary, when two phases are present, addition or removal of heat merely changes the relative amounts of the two phases but does not change the temperature of the system. Regardless of the relative amounts of liquid and gas, the temperature is constant throughout the system and each of the two phases is in thermal equilibrium. In addition, as long as no heat is added or removed from the system, the relative amounts of the two phases are independent of time and are in equilibrium with each other. It should be pointed out that thermal equilibrium differs from phase equilibrium. In fact, we can have systems in which there is thermal equilibrium without phase equilibrium. These two kinds are more accurately called, respectively, *homogeneous* equilibrium and *heterogeneous* equilibrium.

Returning to our experiment, as we continue to remove heat from the liquid, the temperature drops smoothly until we reach the boundary between the liquid and solid regions. At this point, a change takes place similar to the one that occurs at the boundary between gas and liquid, except the phases involved are the liquid and solid, and the boundary itself is the freezing, or melting-point, curve. The heat required to transform one mole of solid at the melting point to liquid at the melting point is called the *latent heat of fusion.*

If we continue to remove more heat, the temperature drops until it approaches absolute zero without the occurrence of any more phases. Also, if we heat the gas above 100°K, no additional phases are encountered.

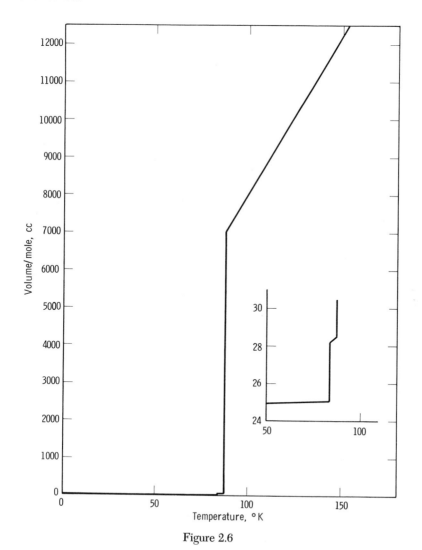

Figure 2.6

In Fig. 2.6, the volume at one atmosphere is plotted as a function of temperature. If we start again at 100°K and lower the temperature, the volume decreases smoothly to the gas-vapor equilibrium point, or boiling point, at 87.4°K, where there is a discontinuous change from the volume of the gas to that of the liquid. On further cooling, the volume of the liquid decreases at a rate much slower than that of the gas, and at the solid-liquid equilibrium point, or freezing point, an additional small discontinuous change is involved. Below this temperature, the volume decreases slowly with decreasing temperature. In going from gas to liquid, the change in volume is very large, indicating that the molecules are much more tightly packed in the liquid than in the gas. The change in volume between liquid and solid is much smaller, which indicates that there is not a very great difference in the packing of the molecules.

If we raise the pressure somewhat and repeat the experiment, we find only a slight change in the temperature of the transition from liquid to solid, but the temperature of the liquid-to-gas transition changes rapidly with changes in the pressure. Increasing the pressure from one to two atmospheres shifts the boiling point from 87.4°K to 94°K. In addition to this shift, the difference in volume of the gas and the liquid at the boiling point as well as the latent heat of vaporization decreases as the pressure is increased, until the pressure reaches 48 atmospheres. This is the *critical pressure* of argon, when both of these quantities are zero and there is no longer any difference between liquid and gas. Above this pressure, there is no temperature at which gas and liquid can be in equilibrium. At pressures above this critical point, there is only a single transition from the solid to a phase best described as *amorphous.* It should be emphasized that this is not a new phase, but an extension of the liquid and gas phases into a region where both are identical.

A question now arises. Is there a similar critical point for the transition from the solid to an amorphous phase? Although no one actually knows the answer at present, it is generally believed that there is no such critical point. At any pressure, it seems that there can be equilibrium between the solid and the amorphous phase at *some* temperature. The data shown on the phase diagram of Fig. 2.3 at extremely high pressures were obtained by Percy W. Bridgman of Harvard University, in an effort to answer this question. In this diagram, it is readily apparent that the application of 5000 atmospheres has shifted the freezing point from 84°K to 180°K without any indication of a critical point. Furthermore, the change in volume at the transition and the latent heat of fusion were measured to an equally high pressure; there was no indication that these quantities were tending to zero, which would be required at a critical point.

Returning now to the usual pressure range around one atmosphere, we should note another fact. At pressures below $\frac{3}{4}$ atm, the pressure at the triple point, it is possible to have gas and solid in equilibrium. This means that if the temperature were raised at constant pressure, solid argon would be converted directly to gas without appearance of the liquid phase. This process is called *sublimation*.

In these experiments, we have covered a wide range of pressures and temperatures in a series of constant pressure paths; that is, paths parallel to the horizontal or temperature scale in the phase diagrams. By plotting the points at which we observed two phases in equilibrium, and connecting these with solid lines, we were able to construct a phase diagram. Another way of obtaining this information is to follow a series of paths parallel to the vertical or pressure scale, that is, constant temperature paths. Let's consider these paths as our second group of experiments.

We want to find out what happens to a fixed mass of argon gas as we raise its pressure while maintaining a constant temperature. For this experiment, we use the same apparatus described previously. In order to vary the pressure, we simply add weight to the piston. To maintain a constant temperature, we insert the apparatus in a bath of liquid, under constant pressure so that it will boil at the desired temperature. As we have noted, the gas and liquid are in equilibrium and we can add or remove heat from such a system without changing the temperature. This makes an excellent constant temperature bath.

We start at 100°K and one atmosphere, the same point as that used in the previous experiment. We could measure both the heat removed from the system and the change in volume, as we did before. However, as we have seen, either one of these parameters will locate the points at which two phases are in equilibrium, and since it is generally simpler to measure the volume, we will consider only this parameter. As we increase the pressure, the volume decreases smoothly, as shown in Fig. 2.7, to a pressure of 3.5 atmospheres. At this point, which cor-

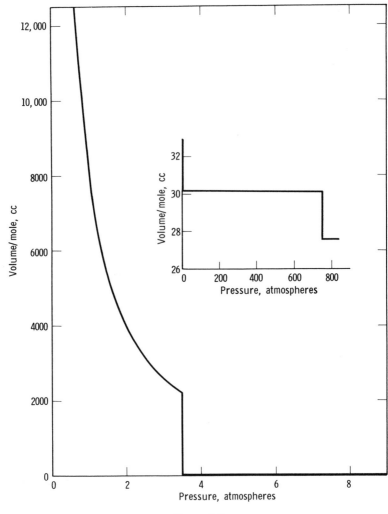

Figure 2.7

responds to the boundary between the liquid and gaseous regions, the gas condenses to liquid with an accompanying change in volume. With further increase in pressure, the volume decreases similarly although much more slowly than in the gas phase until at 750 atmospheres we cross the boundary between liquid and solid. At this point there is a small drop in volume, and further increase in pressure discloses no new phases. As we repeat this experiment at higher and higher temperatures, there is less and less change in volume in going from gas to liquid until, finally, at the critical temperature of 150°K there is no volume change. This temperature and the critical pressure, which we determined earlier, are designated the critical point, and at either higher pressure or higher temperature it is impossible to have gas and liquid in equilibrium.

These two groups of experiments give essentially the same result: location of the points at which the paths of constant pressure or constant temperature intersect one of the lines indicating where two phases are in equilibrium.

Now let's consider another experiment in which the path actually follows one of the lines. Our apparatus, shown schematically in Fig. 2.8, consists of a container of fixed volume, provisions for measuring temperature and pressure, and a pump for removing some of the gas. (The actual equipment is far more complicated.) We start with a part of the apparatus filled with liquid and the remainder filled with gas. Since the two phases are in equilibrium, we can determine a point on the liquid-gas equilibrium line by measuring the temperature and pressure. Next, we remove some of the gas with the pump. The sys-

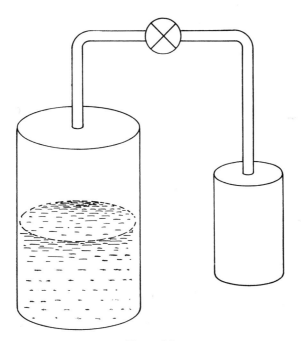

Figure 2.8

tem will no longer be in equilibrium, and in order to restore the equilibrium some of the liquid must evaporate. When the liquid evaporates, heat is absorbed. Since the system is isolated from its surroundings, the only source of heat is the system itself, and thus the whole system will cool off, finally coming to equilibrium at a lower temperature. By measuring the temperature and pressure at which equilibrium is established, we determine a second point on the liquid-gas equilibrium line. This procedure can be continued until we reach the triple point. At this point, there will be solid, liquid, and gas in equilibrium; further pumping will give points along the solid-gas equilibrium line. This method is commonly used to determine the liquid-gas and solid-gas equilibrium lines at moderate temperatures and pressures, but it cannot be used to establish the liquid-solid equilibrium line.

When we first examined the phase diagram, we saw that there were certain regions where only one phase was present. Lines indicated when two phases were in equilibrium, and a point showed that three

(Westinghouse Electric Corporation.)

Pencil portrait of Josiah Willard Gibbs (1839–1903), professor of mathematical physics at Yale College from 1871 until his death. In 1878, Professor Gibbs announced his new interpretation of physical chemistry in a paper published in two installments. Few chemists understood his rigorous mathematical treatment, and it was many years before the implications of his work were recognized. It is now conceded that his "Phase Rule" did for chemistry what Newton's "Law of Gravitation" did for astronomy.

phases were in equilibrium. These observations about the number of phases that can be in equilibrium at a given point in the phase diagram were elegantly summarized by Josiah Willard Gibbs of Yale University. He first published his celebrated Phase Rule in 1876, but it was developed in such rigorous mathematical terms that its value to chemists eluded recognition for many years. In spite of his extreme modesty, it appears that Gibbs was quite aware of the importance of his own work. However, it is doubtful that he realized how greatly it was to influence subsequent developments of chemistry, geology, and metallurgy.

The Phase Rule is expressed by a simple equation:

$$F = C - P + 2,$$

where F is the number of *degrees of freedom*, a term explained below, C is the number of components, and P is the number of phases in equilibrium. There is only one component, argon, for the system we are considering, and therefore C equals one. In any of the regions labeled solid, liquid, or gas, there is only a single phase present, and therefore

$$F = 1 - 1 + 2 = 2.$$

Two degrees of freedom means that we can make small independent changes in the two variables, temperature and pressure, and still remain in the one-phase region. Along the lines separating the single-phase regions, there are two phases in equilibrium, and

$$F = 1 - 2 + 2 = 1.$$

One degree of freedom means that we cannot vary the temperature and pressure independently; instead, for a given change in pressure we must also change the temperature to maintain the two phases in equilibrium. At the triple point, there are three phases in equilibrium, and

$$F = 1 - 3 + 2 = 0.$$

Zero degrees of freedom means it is not possible to make any changes in temperature and pressure and still maintain the three phases.

Since these results seem rather obvious, of what use is the Phase Rule? Let's consider its use in a less obvious case. In a material having more than one solid phase, we might expect to have a phase diagram, as shown in Fig. 2.9a, with the four phases in equilibrium. From the Phase Rule, we have

$$F = 1 - 4 + 2 = -1.$$

Since F is negative, this means that such a point cannot exist. The correct phase diagram for a material having two solid phases is shown in Fig. 2.9b. Here the various phases meet along lines or at triple points, and at no points are there four phases in equilibrium.

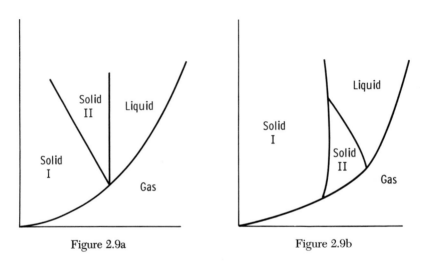

Figure 2.9a   Figure 2.9b

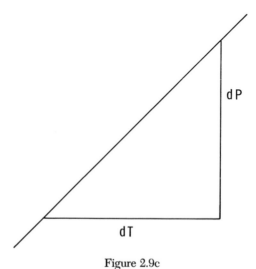

Figure 2.9c

As mentioned previously, when two phases are in equilibrium, the temperature and the pressure are no longer independent variables. The relation between these quantities is given by the Clapeyron equation

$$\frac{dP}{dT} = \frac{l}{T(V_1 - V_2)},$$

where $\frac{dP}{dt}$ is the slope of the two-phase equilibrium line (the change in pressure that must be made in order to return to the line after a small change in temperature), as shown in Fig. 2.9c, l is the latent heat of the transition, T the absolute temperature, and V_1 and V_2 are the molar volumes of the two phases in equilibrium. From data shown in Figs. 2.5 and 2.6, we can calculate the slopes of the solid-liquid and liquid-gas lines at one atmosphere pressure. For the solid-liquid transformation, we have $V_2 = 28.2$ cc/mole, $V_1 = 25.03$ cc/mole, $l = 270$ calories/mole, and $T = 83.9°$K. Substituting these numbers into the Clapeyron equation and multiplying l by 41.30 cc atm/cal to convert to cc atmospheres, we find for $\frac{dP}{dt}$ in atmospheres per degree Kelvin

$$\frac{dP}{dt} = \frac{270 \times 41.30}{83.9(28.20 - 25.03)} = 41.9 \text{ atms/}°\text{K}.$$

We see from Fig. 2.6 that this is the initial slope of the solid-liquid equilibrium. For the liquid-gas line, we have

$$\frac{dP}{dt} = \frac{1500 \times 41.30}{87.4(7000 - 28.5)} = 1.02 \text{ atms/}°\text{K},$$

which agrees with the observed slope of the liquid-vapor curve at one atmosphere. The principal reason for the smaller slope in the liquid-gas equilibrium is that there is a greater change in volume on vaporization than there is on fusion.

Using this discussion of the significance and construction of a phase diagram as a background, let's now examine the phase diagrams of a few familiar substances. First, that of sulfur is shown in Fig. 2.10. In this instance, there are two different solid phases and the diagram is composed of a series of lines joined by triple points, as required by the Phase Rule.

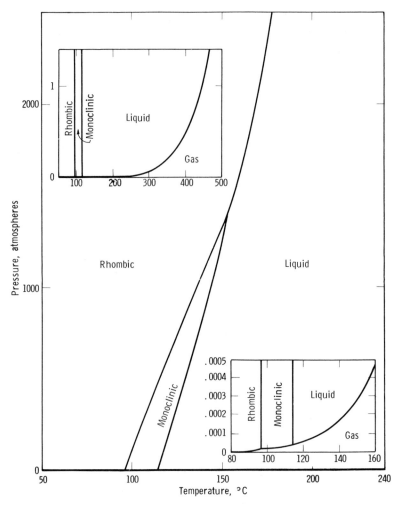

Figure 2.10

At room temperature, 25°C, and one atmosphere, the stable phase
is the material called *rhombic* sulfur. When sulfur is heated, at 96.4°C
it transforms into the second phase, a modification having a different
crystal structure and called *monoclinic* sulfur. On further heating,
sulfur melts at 114°C, and finally boils at 456°C. If the procedure is
reversed and sulfur slowly cooled, the monoclinic modification forms
as the liquid solidifies, and then transforms to the rhombic phase at
96.4°C. However, when monoclinic sulfur is cooled very rapidly to
room temperature, it does not transform to the rhombic phase. In this

case, we have what is known as a *metastable* phase, which is not truly stable, but transforms so slowly to the stable phase that it can be treated as if it were, indeed, a stable phase. The transformation of metastable monoclinic sulfur to stable rhombic sulfur is extremely slow at room temperature. As the temperature is raised, the transformation takes place with increasing rapidity; it is most rapid just below 96.4°C. Above this temperature, the monoclinic phase is stable and there is no tendency to transform to the rhombic phase.

A final interesting point about sulfur is that it is possible to go directly from the liquid to the rhombic form by heating the liquid to 160°C, raising the pressure to 1500 atm, then cooling to 25°C at constant pressure, and finally lowering the pressure to one atmosphere. This path does not cross the monoclinic region and the liquid is directly transformed to the rhombic phase. It is believed that the large crystals of naturally occurring rhombic sulfur were formed by such a process.

Next let's consider carbon; part of the phase diagram is shown in Fig. 2.11. We notice immediately that graphite is the stable phase under normal conditions and diamond is the metastable phase. Under ordinary conditions, the transformation of diamond to graphite is so slow that no change could be detected even in the time since the diamond was formed in the earth many millions of years ago. How-

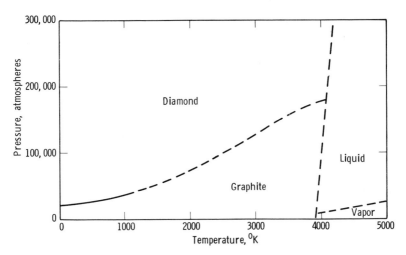

Figure 2.11 The dotted lines in this diagram indicate approximate locations of phase boundaries.

(Courtesy of General Electric Research Laboratory, Schenectady, New York.)

The 1000-ton press used at General Electric Research Laboratory to achieve high pressures. In this apparatus, man-made diamonds were first produced.

(Courtesy of General Electric Research Laboratory, Schenectady, New York.)

Photomicrograph of man-made diamonds.

ever, when diamond is heated to about 1500°C at one atmosphere, the transformation to graphite is quite rapid.

Before this particular phase diagram was known, many attempts were made to convert graphite into diamond at pressures and temperatures in the graphite region. All failed. Recently, man-made diamonds have been produced at roughly 2000°C and pressures of 100,000 atmospheres. Referring to the phase diagram, we notice that these temperatures and pressures are in the diamond region.

Finally, let's examine the phase diagram of water, shown in Figs. 2.12 and 2.13. Looking first at Fig. 2.12, we notice two familiar facts immediately. At one atmosphere, water freezes at 0°C and boils at 100°C. But we get some idea how really complicated this familiar substance is when we look at Fig. 2.13. We see the six different forms of ice mentioned earlier—Ice I, Ice II, Ice III, and so on. At one time

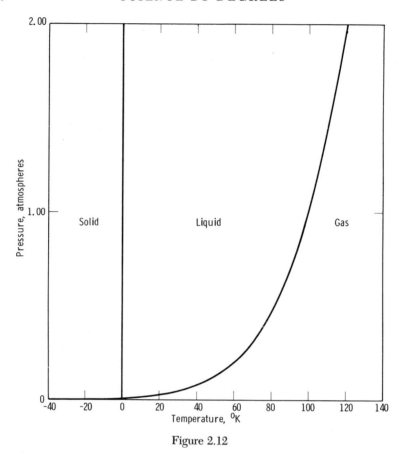

Figure 2.12

it was believed that there was another phase between Ice III and Ice V, and the name Ice IV was reserved for it. Further experiments showed, however, that such a phase did not exist, and the name has not been used for any other stable phase. Ice I is ordinary ice with which we are all well acquainted; this phase is stable at a pressure of one atmosphere.

We notice that in the diagram the phases are bounded by lines and triple points, as required by the Phase Rule for a one-component system. If we were investigating this diagram at high temperatures, where water dissociates into hydrogen and oxygen according to the equation

$$H_2O \rightleftharpoons H_2 + \tfrac{1}{2}O_2,$$

we would have to consider it a two-component system. Another interesting point illustrated by the diagram is that Ice II can never be in equilibrium with the liquid.

When we examine this diagram closely, we see that it differs from the other diagrams we have considered. The boundary between the liquid and solid Ice I slopes the wrong way. That is, if the pressure is increased, the melting point will decrease rather than increase. This fact is related to a familiar property of water—ice floats in water. It means that ice is less dense than water; that is, the molar volume of the solid is greater than that of the liquid. When we substitute the molar volume of liquid (18.019 cc/mole) and solid (19.640 cc/mole), and the latent heat of fusion (1436 cal/mole) into the Clapeyron equation, we find that

$$\frac{dP}{dt} = \frac{1436 \times 41.30}{273.2(18.019 - 19.64)} = -134 \text{ atms/}°\text{K}.$$

Thus, because Ice I is less dense than water, an increase in pressure causes a decrease in its melting point. As pressure is increased, we come to Ice III, a phase more dense than the liquid, and the melting point curve has the usual positive slope.

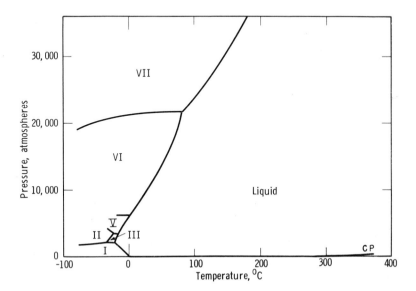

Figure 2.13 The termination of the line between liquid and vapor (CP) is a true critical point. The termination of the other lines (at left) indicates the lack of experimental data, and is of no particular significance.

It has often been suggested that we are able to skate on ice because of the negative slope of the melting point curve. In other words, this explanation assumes that the pressure of the skate's blade on the ice is sufficient to liquefy some of the ice and this film of liquid provides a smooth surface on which the blade slides. However, on the basis of the phase diagram, it can readily be seen that this explanation is incomplete since it is possible to skate at temperatures below $-21\,^{\circ}$C. In the phase diagram, we notice that no amount of pressure will liquefy ice at this temperature. The true explanation probably involves a difference in the bonding of the water molecules on the surface of the ice and those in the bulk.

Now that we have seen how the phase diagram enables us to decide which phase or phases will be present in a substance at a particular temperature and pressure, let's return to argon and investigate its properties in more detail.

Although the behavior of argon is the simplest of any real substance, many of the details are still not completely understood. There are two questions we would like to answer. First, how does the structure, that is, the arrangement of the atoms, differ among the three phases? Second, in what particular region of a phase diagram would we expect to find a given phase?

Before discussing phases, we need to know something about the forces between argon atoms. Argon is in the group of elements called *rare gases*. This group includes helium, He; neon, Ne; argon, A; krypton, Kr; xenon, Xe; and radon, Rn—all of which have their electrons arranged in spherical, symmetric, closed shells. One consequence of this arrangement is that these elements do not readily form any chemical compounds, and this accounts for the inertness of argon mentioned earlier. More important to our present discussion is the fact that the force between argon atoms is only a function of the distance between their centers; it does not depend on any angles. Also, the force between any two argon atoms does not depend on the location of any other argon atoms, at least to a good approximation. This force has been determined by a number of indirect methods, and the results agree reasonably well. One such curve, believed to be essentially correct, is shown in Fig. 2.14.

We can see that for large distances, that is, more than about 9 Å, the force is approximately zero. For smaller distances, say 4 to 5 Å,

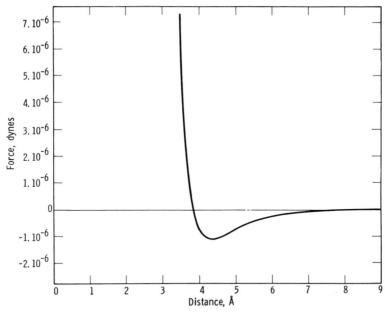

Figure 2.14

the force is large and negative. The argon atoms are attracted to each other by a negative force. As we will see, this attractive force is largely responsible for the formation of the condensed phases, liquid and solid. At 3.8 Å, the force is zero, and at smaller distances there is a large repulsive force. If it were not for this repulsive force, argon would simply collapse into a material having no volume whatever.

For some purposes, it is possible to use a simple model of the forces between atoms. In this *hard sphere model*, the attractive force is neglected and the atoms are considered incompressible spheres with a radius slightly smaller than that for which the force is zero. This is roughly 3.8 Å for argon.

Solid argon is composed of crystals whose atoms are arranged in an orderly fashion. To illustrate, a model of an argon crystal can be constructed by arranging on a board a layer of balls, each representing an argon atom, as shown in Fig. 2.15. In the first layer, each ball touches six other balls. A second layer is arranged on top of the first, as shown in Fig. 2.16, and each ball in this second layer lies above a space in the first layer but makes contact with three balls in the first layer and with six in the second layer. A third layer is placed on the second, as

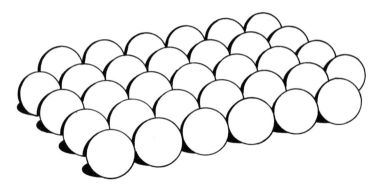

Figure 2.15

Figure 2.16

Figure 2.17

shown in Fig. 2.17, in such a way that the centers of the balls are above the remaining vacant spaces in the first layer. Each ball in the second layer is now in contact with three balls in the third layer and in contact with a total of twelve balls. The arrangement of these twelve nearest neighbors is shown in Fig. 2.18. The fourth layer is arranged directly over the first, and the sequence of layers is repeated indefinitely.

This model of an argon crystal differs from a real crystal in only two respects. In reality, the atoms are not fixed rigidly to the lattice points, but rather vibrate about the position where the forces between atoms is zero. The amplitude of vibration is small at very low temperatures, but it increases as the temperature is raised toward the melting point. In a real argon crystal, not all possible sites are occupied; some remain vacant. The number of these vacancies increases as the temperature is increased.

The liquid differs from the solid in that the molecules are no longer bound to lattice sites, but are free to move throughout the body of the material. Let's imagine a box whose volume is considerably smaller than the volume of a hard sphere equivalent of an argon atom, fixed at some point in a mass of liquid argon. Since the argon atoms are in motion, the centers of the various atoms will drift through the imaginary box. If we determine the fraction of time the center of an argon atom lies within the box, we find that this fraction is independent of the position of the box in the mass of argon. (This is not quite true if the box is very near the walls of the container, so we consider only the bulk of the material.)

If we allow this box to move in such a way that it is always a fixed distance from one particular argon atom, as indicated in Fig. 2.19, we

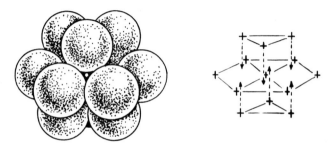

Figure 2.18

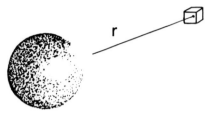

Figure 2.19

obtain very different results. In this case, we find that the fraction of time the center of another argon atom lies within the box is a function of the distance r between the chosen atom's center and the center of the box. The ratio of these two quantities, that is, the fraction of time the center of an argon atom lies within the box, which is maintained a fixed distance from a chosen argon atom, divided by the fraction of time the box would be occupied if it were fixed in the mass of argon, is called the *radial distribution function*. This quantity can be determined by the liquid's diffraction of x rays. The technique is rather complicated and of no particular interest to us here. However, the results obtained for argon at various temperatures are shown in Fig. 2.20. The temperature and pressure at which these curves have been determined are shown in the phase diagram in Fig. 2.20, where the pressure-temperature coordinates of each curve are denoted by the letters A-F. We see that curves A-E were taken in the liquid along the liquid-vapor equilibrium curve, and F was taken in the gas near the critical point.

Let's first examine curve A, which was determined at the lowest temperature and pressure. We notice that the radial distance function is zero for distances less than 3.2 Å. This means that the centers of two argon atoms never get closer than 3.2 Å, which is reasonable considering the large force (Fig. 2.14) required to bring the centers this close together. At about 3.8 Å there is a prominent peak in the radial distribution function. This is just the distance at which the force between argon atoms is zero and at which there are twelve nearest neighbors in the solid. If we calculate the average number of argon atoms whose centers are between 3.4 Å and 4.4 Å from the center atom, we find 10.6 atoms in this spherical shell as compared to 12 atoms found in the solid. Following this peak, we notice first a region containing less than the average number of argon atoms, and

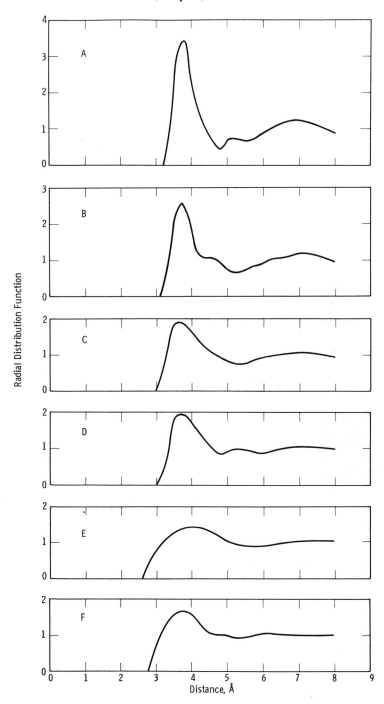

Figure 2.20

then another peak. We see that in the liquid the atoms are arranged in shells, the first rather well-defined and successive ones more and more diffuse, until finally the atoms are randomly distributed. We also have these same shells in the ideal model of the solid, but they are sharply defined throughout the crystal. We can distinguish between two kinds of orders: *long-range order,* as in a crystal where the positions of atoms are ordered over long distances, and *short-range order,* as in a liquid where only the first few neighbors are ordered.

As we examine curves B through E, which correspond to the liquid at higher temperature and pressure, we see that they are similar, although they follow certain trends with increased temperature. The distance at which the radial distribution function goes to zero decreases as the temperature is increased. This is due partly to the higher pressure, which tends to bring all the molecules closer together, and partly to the higher temperatures that induce the atoms to move faster, thus allowing them to get closer together. The height of the first peak decreases and the other peaks rapidly become "smeared out," indicating less order as the temperature is raised.

At high temperature and low pressure, the gas is quite different from the liquid and the solid. In argon gas at ordinary temperature and pressure, 25°C and one atmosphere, the molecules are 37 Å apart on the average. This means that an individual molecule moves about almost completely independent of the others. Under these conditions, gas behaves as an ideal gas, obeying the simple relation between pressure, temperature, and volume, known as the *ideal gas law.* This is expressed by the equation

$$PV = RT,$$

where R is the gas constant, equal to 82.06 cc $\cdot$ atm/(mole)(°K). The expression is valid for all gases provided the only interaction between molecules is simple elastic collisions. As the molecules are brought closer together, the attractive force becomes important, and the volume of the gas is somewhat smaller than calculated from the ideal gas law. For even less separation, the repulsive force becomes important, and the calculated volume is larger than the observed volume. These effects are shown in Fig. 2.21, where $V_{observed}/V_{calculated}$ is plotted against the pressure at a constant temperature of 273°K. We notice that for low pressure, corresponding to large distances between mole-

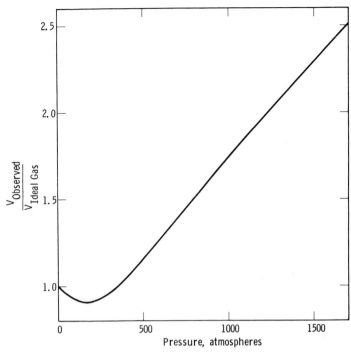

Figure 2.21

cules, the quantity is unity, which shows that the ideal gas law is obeyed. Furthermore, for higher pressures, the quantity first decreases, then increases, as predicted above. For this particular curve, which was measured far above the critical point of $151°K$, the minimum is quite shallow. As the temperature is lowered and approaches the critical temperature, the minimum becomes deeper. Below the critical temperature, the gas condenses to a liquid, with the discontinuous change in volume indicated in Figs. 2.6 and 2.7.

The arrangement of molecules in the gas is completely random in regions where the ideal gas law is obeyed. As the temperature is lowered, the molecules form clusters or groups of atoms in which each is within range of the attractive force of at least one other atom in the group. This distance is roughly 4 Å for argon. The first clusters formed are pairs and, as the temperature is lowered, triplets and larger groups become abundant, until finally condensation takes place with formation of the liquid phase, which essentially is one large cluster. It should be pointed out that at no time is the gas composed of a single type of cluster, such as pairs, but is always a mixture of several types ranging from single atoms to the largest clusters that are stable at the particular temperature and pressure.

We can summarize the effect of temperature on the structure of matter in a simple statement: The higher the temperature, the less ordered the arrangement of atoms. At low temperatures, there is a particular site for each atom in the solid. As temperature is raised toward the melting point, the atoms begin to vibrate with somewhat greater amplitude than at very low temperatures. Occasionally, a site is vacant, so the heated solid is less ordered than it is at low temperatures. The liquid is considerably less ordered than the solid, and we cannot say where a given atom is located; we can only state that a given atom has some average number of neighbors within a certain distance. The gas phase is similar to the liquid but more disordered; as we tend toward higher temperatures there is less and less correlation between the positions of the atoms, until finally the position of any atom is almost completely independent of all others. The tiny bit of order that remains is the result of the large repulsive forces between atoms at small distances apart. The centers of the atoms cannot get closer than, say, roughly 3 Å, in the case of argon. The effect of increasing pressure, however, is to bring the atoms closer together, and thus, because of the forces between the atoms, increasing pressure increases the order of the arrangement. Therefore, a small increase in pressure tends to nullify the effects of a small increase in temperature.

It will be recalled that the second of our two questions was, "In what particular region of a phase diagram would we expect to find a given phase?" Generally speaking, the more ordered structures occur in the upper left-hand corner of the phase diagram, as shown in Fig. 2.11, that is, the region of high pressure and low temperature. The least ordered structures occur in the opposite or lower right-hand corner— the area of high temperature and low pressure. In the regions between these two extremes, there is decreasing order from upper left to lower right. For example, in the phase diagram for carbon, shown in Fig. 2.11, we find diamond in the upper left-hand corner, then graphite, which is still solid carbon but with a less ordered crystal structure than that of diamond. Continuing toward the lower right-hand corner of the diagram, we next have liquid, which is less ordered than solid, and finally there is gas, the least ordered of all these phases.

PART 2

The Inside Story

The Microscopic
View

IN THE FIRST CHAPTER, we concluded that temperature is simply the macroscopic property of matter that allows us to discuss conveniently the equilibrium between two bodies. Now we want to investigate the same ideas from a microscopic point of view, and this requires setting up more detailed models of the substances we are going to consider. Suppose we enter the microscopic world.

*We begin with a solid, selecting one composed of a simple cubic lattice of atoms, as shown in Fig. 3.1. Each atom is at its equilibrium position, that is, its time-averaged position. Let's think of each atom as bound to its lattice site in a manner similar to that of the ball in Fig. 3.2. This ball will remain at its equilibrium position, $x = 0$, $y = 0$, if no external forces are applied. If we give the ball some energy, however—by striking it, for example—it will vibrate in some manner about $x = 0$, $y = 0$. Now intuition tells us that the energy of this ball can be any quantity from zero up to some maximum, dictated by the strength of the springs. Unfortunately, although our intuition is essentially correct for macroscopic objects such as balls, it fails abysmally for small particles such as electrons and atoms. For it has

* The treatment given here is patterned after that of R. W. Gurney in Introduction to Statistical Mechanics.

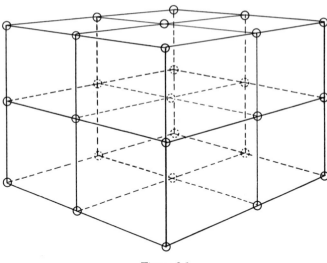

Figure 3.1

been found that in order to explain many phenomena of the microscopic world, it is necessary to assume that a particle can take only
certain values of energy, denoted by E. The calculation of the values
of these energy levels is the subject of quantum theory; however, for
our present purposes, we will simply assume that we know the energy
values that are possible for the atom. We can introduce energy level
diagrams, indicated in Fig. 3.3, where each horizontal line designates
a possible value of the energy. In this case, all levels will be considered
equally spaced, although actually this is not always true. The spacing
of level u depends mainly on the mass of the particle and the strength
of the forces that tend to keep the atom at its equilibrium position.
Our principal problem will be to determine how many of the atoms
of the solid are found to possess each of the possible energy values.

Let's first consider a solid composed of only three atoms. We will
think of this solid as being held together by small springs, as in Fig.
3.4. In this way, it is possible for energy to be transferred from one
particle to another. Then let's assume that the total energy of these
three particles is exactly $3u$—u being the spacing between energy
levels. In Fig. 3.5, we see how the three particles might be arranged
so that the total energy is $3u$. It is of the greatest importance to recognize that distribution a can arise in more than one way. (A distribution will be defined by giving the number of particles in each

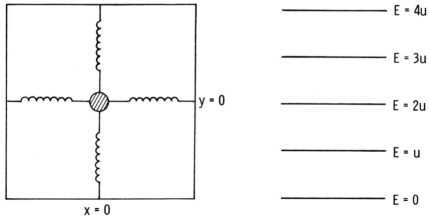

Figure 3.2

Figure 3.3

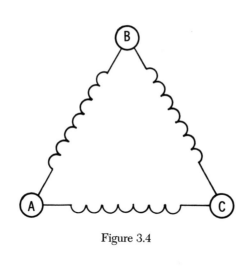

Figure 3.4

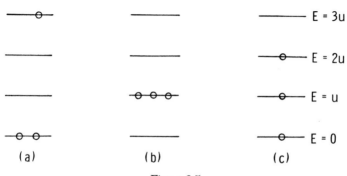

Figure 3.5

energy level.) For example, if we label the three atoms A, B, and C, we can have either A, B, or C in the top level. Thus distribution *a* can arise in three different ways. Stated somewhat more precisely, distribution *a* is made up of three *configurations*. For distribution *c*, it can be seen that there are three choices for the upper level, and therefore two choices for the middle level; finally, there is one choice for the lower level, giving six configurations in all. This means that distribution *b* can come about in only one way. The question that naturally arises is which of these configurations actually exists in nature. As we have already mentioned, the fundamental difficulty in the microscopic world is that we have no means of direct observation. We have no way of telling which of the above ten configurations corresponds to reality. At this point, we must frankly admit our ignorance and assume that all ten are equally probable. Furthermore, since these particles interact with one another, energy may be transferred from one particle to another. Thus, in time we might expect all ten configurations to occur with equal frequency. In fact, we will make just this assumption. Often, in science, it is necessary to make such blatant assumptions, whose only justification is that they may lead to a correct result. Using the above assumptions, we can easily calculate the average number of particles in each energy level. For example, let's examine the level $E = 0$. We see that distribution *a* occurs 3/10 of the total time, and distribution *c* occurs 6/10 of the total time. This means that 6/10 of the time the level $E = 0$ contains one particle, 3/10 of the time it contains two particles, and, finally, 1/10 of the time it is empty. Therefore, the level $E = 0$ contains on the average 12/10 particles. The results for the remaining levels are shown in the following table, 3.A.

TABLE 3.A

Level	Average number of particles
$E = 3u$	3/10
$E = 2u$	6/10
$E = u$	9/10
$E = 0$	12/10

The important result is that the average population of each energy level becomes less as we go up in energy. We will see shortly that this is a fundamental result, valid for any number of particles.

Let's now introduce the symbol ω to denote the number of configurations making up a distribution. We have already seen that for (a) $\omega = 3$, (b) $\omega = 1$, (c) $\omega = 6$. Therefore, the most probable distribution at any given time will be c. Of course, in this case, the other two distributions will be met quite frequently. However, we will see that as the number of particles is increased, there will be one particular distribution that occurs so often that all others may be neglected.

HOW TO COUNT CONFIGURATIONS

Before continuing, it will be useful to derive a mathematical technique for counting the number of different configurations leading to the same energy distribution. As we have mentioned, a distribution is defined by giving the number of particles in each energy level. A given distribution is made up of a number of configurations, a configuration being defined by telling *which* particles are in each level. Consider Fig. 3.5(c). We may argue as follows: Either atom A, B, or C can go into level $E = 0$. Either of the two remaining atoms can go into $E = u$, and one can go into $E = 2u$. Thus, the number of configurations is

$$\omega = 3 \times 2 \times 1 = 6.$$

This may be written $\omega = 3!$, where 3! is read *factorial* 3. Thus,

$$3! = 3 \times 2 \times 1.$$

In general, we have

$$n! = n(n - 1)(n - 2) \ldots 2 \times 1. \tag{3.1}$$

In the following, we will frequently need the value 0!. More advanced treatments show that $0! = 1$. We will simply accept this result. Now consider Fig. 3.5(a). We no longer have six configurations, because although there are three choices for the level at $3u$, there is only one way to put the remaining two particles in level 0. The results may be written

$$\omega = \frac{3!}{2!} = 3.$$

In fact, we may write in general

$$\omega = \frac{n!}{n_1! \, n_2! \, n_3! \ldots n_h!}, \tag{3.2}$$

where n is the total number of particles, n_1 is the number in level 1, etc., n_h is the number in the highest occupied level. Ambition or curiosity may suggest verifying this expression in some simple cases.

FINDING THE MOST PROBABLE DISTRIBUTION

We may now return to the main thread of the argument and consider, for example, twenty particles having fifteen units of energy. Referring to the two distributions of Fig. 3.6, for distribution a we find $\omega = 1$, and for b we find $\omega = 1.5 \times 10^8$. Obviously, distribution a can be neglected in any considerations of the properties of this system. Suppose, for example, the system exists at some point in time in a distribution with $\omega = 10^3$. By collisions, it will change to another distribution. The first question is how will ω change. It is clear intuitively that it is always most probable for the system to change in such a way as to increase ω. This is a general principle.

If we look again at our two "solids," one composed of three particles and the other of twenty particles, we notice a most interesting difference. In the case of three particles, all distributions had to be considered, since all occurred with reasonable frequency. This means the number of particles in any given level fluctuates very greatly in time. However, in the case of twenty particles, we see that the probability of finding some distributions is only one ten-millionth of the probability of finding one of the more popular ones. This tends to reduce the amount of fluctuation in the population of any given level. We might hope that as the number of particles in a solid is increased, the fluctuation in the population of a given level continues to decrease

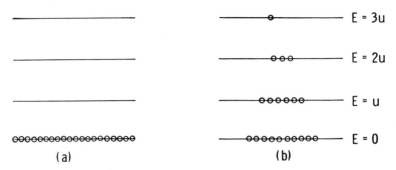

Figure 3.6

and that by the time we reach solids of normal size (containing say 10^{22} atoms) the fluctuations are negligible. Is this actually the case?

Let's consider a solid composed of 10^{22} particles, for example. We first ask what distribution gives the maximum value of ω. We would then like to be able to show that any distribution in which the number of particles per level is significantly different from that of the maximum must have negligible values of ω.

At this point, we need to introduce a little more mathematical apparatus in order to find the maximum value of ω. A system of three levels containing n particles and a total energy E will serve the purpose. We may write

$$\omega = \frac{n!}{n_0!\, n_1!\, n_2!}. \tag{3.3}$$

Of course, we have two requirements. First, we know that the total number of particles in all levels must equal N. We write this as

$$n_0 + n_1 + n_2 = N. \tag{3.4}$$

Also the total energy must be equal to E, and

$$n_0 E_0 + n_1 E_1 + n_2 E_2 = E. \tag{3.5}$$

Let's consider some initial distribution with values $n_0 = n_0'$, $n_1 = n_1'$, $n_2 = n_2'$. Thus,

$$\omega_{\text{initial}} = \frac{n!}{n_0'!\, n_1'!\, n_2'!}. \tag{3.6}$$

Now, in Fig. 3.6, if we take two particles from level 1, placing one in level 0 and the other in level 2, we will not have changed the total energy in the system or the number of particles. Thus, the above conditions of Eqs. 3.4 and 3.5 are satisfied, and we have

$$\omega_{\text{final}} = \frac{n!}{(n_0' + 1)!\, (n_1' - 2)!\, (n_2' + 1)!}, \tag{3.7}$$

and then

$$\frac{\omega_{\text{final}}}{\omega_{\text{initial}}} = \frac{n_1'(n_1' - 1)}{(n_0' + 1)(n_2' + 1)}. \tag{3.8}$$

However, since the primed n's are of the order of 10^{19}, the unity may be neglected in each parenthesis. Therefore,

$$\frac{\omega_f}{\omega_i} = \frac{n_1{}^2}{n_0 n_2}. \tag{3.9}$$

If this ratio is greater than one, ω has been increased by this transferal of particles. We may then repeat the process to see if the ratio is again greater than unity; that is, to see if we are still moving in the direction of increasing ω. After movement of a certain number of particles, the ratio will become less than unity. This, of course, means that we are creating distributions of lower ω. This argument leads us to conclude that maximum ω is achieved when the ratio of $\omega_f/\omega_i = 1$; that is,

$$n_1{}^2 = n_0 n_2. \tag{3.10}$$

This same law will now also hold for any set of three consecutive levels. It is well worth investigating the situation in the case where the levels are not equally spaced. (If $E_2 - E_1 = u$, and $E_1 - E_0 = v$, we may satisfy the conditions of Eqs. 3.4 and 3.5 by placing n particles in level 2 and m particles in level 0 such that $um = vn$.) However, for the moment, let's suppose that our system has only equally spaced levels. Then we know that at equilibrium the population of the levels must fulfill three conditions:

$$n_1{}^2 = n_0 n_2,$$
$$n_0 + n_1 + n_2 = N,$$
$$n_1 E_1 + n_2 E_2 = E.$$

The second criterion is that the number of particles is fixed, and the third is that the total energy is fixed. Actually, it must be remembered that Eq. 3.9 was derived using conditions of conservation of energy and number of particles; that is, in the transfer process used to derive Eq. 3.10, the number of particles and the quantity of energy was held fixed. Thus, the last two of the three equations above only serve the purpose of fixing the number of particles and the quantity of energy. We now need to solve Eq. 3.10.

When we consider the following properties of exponents

$$R^{-\mu x} R^{-\mu y} = R^{-\mu(x+y)},$$

we see immediately that if we assume that

$$n_i \propto R^{-\mu E_i} \tag{3.11}$$

(the sign $\propto$ means that n_i is directly proportional to $R^{-\mu E_i}$), the condition of Eq. 3.10 is satisfied, since

$$\frac{n_1{}^2}{n_0 n_2} = \frac{(R^{-\mu E_1})^2}{R^{-\mu E_0} \times R^{-\mu E_2}} = \frac{R^{-2\mu u}}{R^0 R^{-2\mu u}} = 1. \tag{3.12}$$

We may now assume that the proportionality constant connecting the two sides of Eq. 3.11 is equal to some constant A. Thus, we have

$$n_i = AR^{\mu E_i}. \tag{3.13}$$

At this point, the solution of Eq. 3.13 does not look very useful, since there are three arbitrary parameters, A, R, and μ. We will see shortly that two of these (A and μ) are needed to satisfy the conditions of Eqs. 3.4 and 3.5. The third parameter R will be *arbitrarily* set equal to e, the base of the Naperian logarithms. (At the end of the present section, we will have enough knowledge to show that the choice of R merely gives an arbitrariness in the temperature scale. Although this is of some interest, we will not carry through the argument.)

Now, using Eq. 3.4, we can evaluate A, because

$$n_0 + n_1 + n_2 = A + Ae^{-\mu u} + Ae^{-2\mu u}.$$

Therefore,

$$A = \frac{N}{1 + e^{-\mu u} + e^{-2\mu u}}. \tag{3.14}$$

In principle, μ may be determined from Eq. 3.5. We will return shortly to the importance of μ. Now, however, it is necessary to say a little more about the equilibrium distribution given by Eq. 3.13. We have argued that our system will tend to assume that distribution which can occur in the maximum number of ways. But before accepting the fact that this is really the distribution we would expect to find *if* we were able to do the experiment, we must show that all other distributions that occur with any reasonable frequency are indistinguishable from the one of the maximum ω, namely, Eq. 3.13. The following argument is developed in detail here for the benefit of those interested in following it, but the results are simply summarized on page 73.

Let's arbitrarily assume that any distribution that has a ω of less than one-billionth of $\omega_{\max}$ is negligible. Thus, we would like to show that any distribution with a ω greater than $10^{-9}\omega_{\max}$ is indistinguishable from a distribution of ω_{max}. We will do this by trying a simple thought experiment. Consider our set of three levels populated according to the rule of Eq. 3.10:

$$n_1{}^2 = n_0 n_2.$$

If we were considering a cubic centimeter of a metal, for example, we would be dealing with perhaps 10^{22} atoms. Thus, we might take $n_0 = 10^{20}$, $n_1 = 10^{21}$, $n_2 = 10^{22}$. These numbers satisfy Eq. 3.10. Now, let's remove particles in pairs from level 1, placing one particle in level 0, and the other in level 2. The energy remains constant as does the number of particles. For the ratio of the final value of ω_f to ω_{max}, we can write

$$\frac{\omega_f}{\omega_{max}} = \frac{N!}{(n_0 - \chi)! \, (n_1 + 2\chi)! \, (n_2 - \chi)!} \times \frac{n_0! \, n_1! \, n_2!}{N!}, \quad (3.15)$$

where 2χ is the total number of particles removed from level 1. As we have already mentioned, our objective is to find the value of χ that will make ω_f/ω_{max} less than 10^{-9}. In order to evaluate this expression, it is necessary to introduce a few approximations. First, we must have an approximation for $n!$. Sterling's approximation for the factorial gives

$$ln \, n! = n ln \, n - n. \quad (3.16)$$

This is valid only for large n. However, even for $n = 10$, we can easily see that this is a good approximation. Also, we will need

$$ln \, (1 + \chi) \sim \chi. \quad (3.17)$$

This is a good approximation for χ less than $1/10$. This relation can be simply checked by looking at a set of tables of natural logarithms. We are now in a position to evaluate ω_f/ω_{max}.

After a considerable amount of rather tedious algebra, using Eqs. 3.16 and 3.17, we may show that

$$ln \frac{\omega_f}{\omega_{max}} = -\frac{\chi^2}{2}\left(\frac{1}{n_0} + \frac{4}{n_1} + \frac{1}{n_2}\right). \quad (3.18)$$

Thus, if $(\omega_f/\omega_{max}) = 10^{-9}$, we have

$$+9 \times 2.3 = +\frac{\chi^2}{2}\left(\frac{1}{10^{20}} + \frac{4}{10^{21}} + \frac{1}{10^{22}}\right)$$

$$\chi = 5 \times 10^9. \quad (3.19)$$

Thus, we would have to move only 10^{10} particles (remember, there are 10^{21} particles in this level) from the middle level to reduce ω by a factor of 10^9. Observe that this change would alter the value of n_0 by only one part in 10 billion—clearly, a negligible quantity. Thus, as far as we are concerned, the distribution described by Eq. 3.10 is the *only* one that need be considered.

Let's now summarize the mathematical results of the preceding analysis. We had shown that the distribution of Eq. 3.10 had the highest values of ω; in other words, it is the most probable one. The question that naturally arose was whether there are significantly different distributions with comparable values of ω. If so, this could greatly complicate further considerations of the microscopic world. Obviously, it is far simpler to consider a single distribution rather than many. However, the mathematical analysis was able to show that all distributions that need to be considered, that is, those with more than one chance in a billion of occurring, for example, are essentially indistinguishable.

RELATIONSHIP OF DISTRIBUTION AND TEMPERATURE

We are now ready to tackle the central problem of this chapter. What happens from the microscopic point of view when we put together two bodies that are initially not in equilibrium with each other? Before we can consider this rather complicated question, we must look into a few details. Suppose, for example, we take a piece of copper from ice water and another piece of copper from boiling water and place them together. We know that energy (heat) will be transferred from the hot body to the cold one. What happens to the value of ω when such heat is transferred? Consider again our set of three levels. If energy is added to the system, some of the particles must be moved to a higher energy level. Let's see what happens to ω if the energy added is just sufficient to raise one atom from E_1 to E_2. We find that

$$\frac{\omega_f}{\omega_{max}} = \frac{N!}{n_0! \, (n_1 - 1)! \, (n_2 + 1)!} \times \frac{n_0! \, n_1! \, n_2!}{N!} = \frac{n_1}{n_2}. \quad (3.20)$$

(Again, we have neglected the unity with respect to n in terms like $(n + 1)$.) Now, if the system is in equilibrium, we have

$$\frac{\omega_f}{\omega_{max}} = \frac{n_1}{n_2} = \frac{Ae^{-\mu E_1}}{Ae^{-\mu E_2}} = e^{+\mu u}. \tag{3.21}$$

We see that the addition of energy increases ω.

Finally, it is necessary to ask what our criteria for equilibrium will be when we put two systems together in thermal contact. The answer must be the same for a single system; that is, the distribution that can arise in the maximum number of ways will be the equilibrium state. It is easy to be convinced that the ω for the joint system ω_T is simply equal to the product of the ω's for the individual systems. Thus, we want to find the criteria for having ω_T a maximum. We allow both systems to have the *same* set of energy levels of spacing u, and let the two distributions be represented by:

$$\text{System 1} \quad n_{1i} = A_1 e^{-\mu_1 E_i};$$

$$\text{System 2} \quad n_{2i} = A_2 e^{-\mu_2 E_i}. \tag{3.22}$$

Remember, we have related A to the total number of particles and to the total energy. There is a similar expression for μ, although we did not derive it. We can see that A and μ need not be the same for the two systems, since neither the total energy nor the total number of particles is necessarily equal. Now let's perform another thought experiment. We transfer one unit of energy from system 1 to system 2, remembering that only energy is transferred; the number of particles in each system remains fixed. We see that ω_T will change. Let's continue transferring energy, one unit at a time, until we reach a point where ω_T does not change. As before, this will be the maximum value of ω_T. We may write

$$\frac{(\omega_T)_{Final}}{(\omega_T)_{Initial}} = \frac{\omega_{1F}\omega_{2F}}{\omega_{1I}\omega_{2I}} = \frac{\omega_{1F}}{\omega_{1I}} \times \frac{\omega_{2F}}{\omega_{2I}}. \tag{3.23}$$

Now, we know from Eq. 3.21 that

$$\frac{\omega_{1F}}{\omega_{1I}} = e^{\mu_1 u},$$

and

$$\frac{\omega_{2F}}{\omega_{2I}} = e^{-\mu_2 u}.$$

Therefore,

$$\frac{\omega_{TF}}{\omega_{TI}} = e^{(\mu_1 - \mu_2)u}. \tag{3.24}$$

The condition for equilibrium is simply that this expression be equal to unity. This can happen only when $\mu_1 = \mu_2$. Thus, ω_T is a maximum when both systems are described by the same value of μ. This is a general result. When any number of systems are brought together, they will eventually reach a state of equilibrium, each system being described by the same value of μ.

We think back now to the macroscopic picture, where we found that all systems in equilibrium could be described by a single parameter, the temperature. We therefore conclude that our parameter μ describing the particle distribution must be solely dependent on the temperature. Actually, this type of argument can take us no further. As we saw in the macroscopic case, the method of assigning a number to the temperature scale was quite arbitrary. We have reached the same point in the microscopic case. Since the macroscopic scale has already been set up, we will define the scale of μ in such a way that it agrees with that scale. If we define the microscopic temperature such that

$$\mu = \frac{1}{kT}, \tag{3.25}$$

where T is the absolute temperature and $k = 1.4 \times 10^{-16}$ ergs/deg, it is found that this definition will always correspond to the macroscopic temperature.

A few final points: It is most important to recognize that the concept of temperature is based on very large numbers. In other words, it is based on the fact that the distribution can be described by a single value of μ. If the number of particles is small enough that other distributions occur with significant frequency, then the temperature cannot be defined.

Before moving on, it is worth mentioning again the concept of ω, the number of ways in which a given distribution can arise. A new quantity may be defined by the relation

$$S = k \, ln \, \omega. \tag{3.26}$$

We then see that equilibrium properties may be found by maximizing the quantity S, instead of ω. This quantity is sometimes very useful; it is called the *entropy*.

RELATIONSHIP OF TEMPERATURE AND HEAT

Let's now turn our attention to the heat capacity, introduced on a macroscopic scale in Chapter One. From our previous experience, we know that we will have to introduce detailed models. Gases, liquids, amorphous solids, and crystalline solids will require different microscopic models for the proper calculation of their properties. In this section, we will calculate the heat capacity of the atoms in a crystalline solid. From Eq. 3.20, we see that we first need to calculate the energy of a solid and its dependence on temperature. The energy, in turn, requires a knowledge of the allowed energy levels for the atom in the solid and, in addition, we need to know the way in which the atoms populate these levels. The developments of the preceding section allow us to determine this latter piece of information; however, it cannot give the allowed energy levels of the atom in the solid. For these, we must resort to quantum mechanics, from which we learn that the energy levels for the atoms in a solid can be approximated by an infinite series of equally spaced levels of spacing ω, which varies from solid to solid. We know from the above discussion that the number of particles n_i in the ith level is given by

$$n_i = A e^{-E_i/kT}.$$

If the total number of atoms in the solid is N, we can easily evaluate A. We find that

$$n_i = \frac{N e^{-E_i/kT}}{\sum\limits_{i=0}^{\infty} e^{-E_i/kT}}. \tag{3.27}$$

The symbol $\sum\limits_{i}$ simply means the sum of terms in which i goes from 0 to ∞. Thus,

$$\sum_{i=0}^{\infty} e^{-E_i/kT} = e^{-E_0/kT} + e^{-E_1/kT} + e^{-E_2/kT} + \cdots.$$

Using Eq. 3.27, the energy of the N atoms can be written as

$$E = n_0 E_0 + n_1 E_1 + n_2 E_2 + \cdots,$$

or using the summation sign Σ, we can write

$$E = \sum_{i=0}^{\infty} n_i E_i = N \frac{\sum_{i=0}^{\infty} E_i e^{-E_i/kT}}{\sum_{i=0}^{\infty} e^{-E_i/kT}}. \tag{3.28}$$

Now, because of the properties of our set of energy levels, we know that

$$E_i = iu. \tag{3.29}$$

Thus,

$$E = \frac{Nu \sum_{i=0}^{\infty} i e^{-iu/kT}}{\sum_{i=0}^{\infty} e^{-iu/kT}}. \tag{3.30}$$

To evaluate this energy, we need to evaluate the two summations. Fortunately, in the present case we can do this by elementary methods. Consider first the denominator. We can write this as

$$\sum_{i=0}^{\infty} e^{-iu/kT} = 1 + e^{-u/kT} + e^{-2u/kT} + e^{-3u/kT} + \cdots, \tag{3.31}$$

which is simply an infinite geometric series of the form $1 + r + r^2 + r^3 + \cdots$, where r is less than 1. Its sum is known to be

$$\sum_{i=0}^{\infty} e^{-iu/kT} = \frac{1}{1 - e^{-u/kT}}. \tag{3.32}$$

This is most easily seen by writing the sum S as

$$S = 1 + r + r^2 + r^3 + \cdots.$$

Then

$$rS = r + r^2 + r^3 + \cdots.$$

The difference of these two sums (for $r < 1$) is then

$$S(1 - r) = 1. \tag{3.33}$$

(Since we have an infinite series and $r < 1$, only the unity appears on the right-hand side.) Thus, we have

$$S = \frac{1}{1 - r}. \tag{3.34}$$

The form of Eq. 3.32 follows immediately.

The numerator is somewhat more difficult to evaluate. Here we have a sum of the form

$$S = r + 2r^2 + 3r^3 + 4r^4 + \cdots. \tag{3.35}$$

To evaluate this sum, we may consider the sum S', as follows:

$$
\begin{aligned}
S' &= r + r^2 + r^3 + r^4 + \cdots \\
rS' &= \phantom{r + {}} r^2 + r^3 + r^4 + \cdots \\
r^2 S' &= \phantom{r + r^2 + {}} r^3 + r^4 + \cdots \\
r^3 S' &= \phantom{r + r^2 + r^3 + {}} r^4 + \cdots \\
r^n S' &= \phantom{r + r^2 + r^3 + r^4 + {}} \cdots.
\end{aligned}
\tag{3.36}
$$

If we now sum both sides of the above infinite set of equations, we find

$$S'(1 + r + r^2 + r^3 + \cdots) = r + 2r^2 + 3r^3 + 4r^4 + \cdots = S. \tag{3.37}$$

Thus

$$S = r(1 + r + r^2 + r^3 + \cdots)^2 = \frac{r}{(1 - r)^2}. \tag{3.38}$$

From this the energy can be written:

$$E = Nu \frac{e^{-u/kT}}{(1 - e^{-u/kT})^2} \times (1 - e^{-u/kT}) = Nu \frac{e^{-u/kT}}{1 - e^{-u/kT}}. \tag{3.39}$$

There are two important cases of this equation to consider. First, let's look at very low temperatures. Our previous knowledge tells us that as we go toward $0°K$, more and more of the atoms will be found in the state $E = 0$. In fact, at $0°K$ all atoms are in this state and the total energy should be equal to zero. An examination of the above expression for the energy shows that our theory does, indeed, give us $E = 0$, for $e^{-\infty}$ is equal to zero.

Another interesting temperature region is the one where T is much greater than u/k. In this case, the exponent occurring in the energy expression is small compared to unity. Hence, we may use an approximate expression

$$e^\chi = 1 + \chi.$$

The correctness of this expression for small χ may be verified with the use of a table of Naperian logarithms. (This approximation is simply the antilogarithm of Eq. 3.32.) Using this approximation, we find that

$$E = \frac{Nu(1 - u/kT)}{u/kT} = NkT\left(1 - \frac{u}{kT}\right). \tag{3.40}$$

Thus, as u/kT becomes much smaller than unity, the energy approaches the value NkT. We see that each atom has an average energy kT. This is an example of the *Equipartition Theorem*.

We now want to evaluate the heat capacity itself. As we have seen in Eq. 1.13,

$$C_v = \frac{\Delta E}{\Delta T}.$$

If the elements of differential calculus are familiar, it will be recognized that the heat capacity is simply the temperature derivative of the energy. If not, however, there is a straightforward way to get the same result. Eq. 3.20 says that

$$C_v = \frac{E(T_2) - E(T_1)}{T_2 - T_1}, \tag{3.41}$$

where, for example, $E(T_2)$ means the energy of the system at temperature T_2. Of course, C_v is dependent on the temperature. Therefore, Eq. 3.41 defines C_v at a temperature T only if the temperatures T_2 and T_1 are very close to T. This gives us the clue. Examine Fig. 3.7, a plot of Eq. 3.39, the total energy of the system versus the tempera-

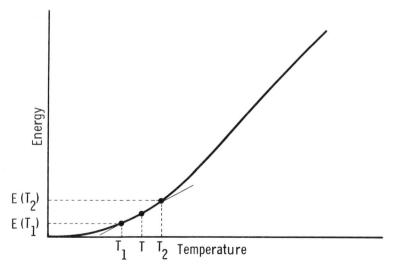

Figure 3.7

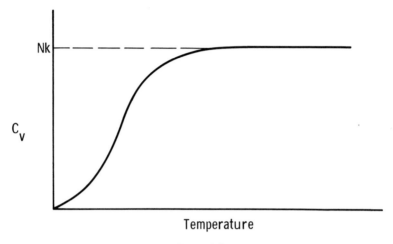

Figure 3.8

ture. Now let's take the temperatures T_1 and T_2 on either side of T. From the graph, we can calculate C_v using Eq. 3.41. In Fig. 3.7, we see that C_v is simply the slope of the straight line through the two points at T_2 and T_1. Now, however, let the points T_1 and T_2 approach T. We see that as T_2 and T_1 approach closer and closer to T, the straight line becomes a better and better approximation to the tangent of the curve. Then, in reality, C_v is only the slope of the tangent to the E versus T curve, at a temperature T. In Fig. 3.8, C_v versus the temperature is plotted. Differential calculus can easily show that the form of this curve is

$$C_v = \frac{dE}{dT} = Nk \left(\frac{u}{kT} \right)^2 \frac{e^{-u/kT}}{(1 - e^{-u/kT})^2}. \tag{3.42}$$

As with the energy expression, there are two interesting regions. These can be seen by examining either Fig. 3.8 or Eq. 3.42. As T approaches $0°$K, we see that C_v approaches zero. This means that a small amount of heat produces a larger temperature change. At higher temperatures, we see that C is independent of T, and equal to Nk. It is worth pursuing this point somewhat further in order to arrive at a well-known result. Although it has not been mentioned explicitly, the calculation above is for the case where the atoms are allowed to move only in one direction. It turns out that if the calculation is done for three dimensions, the heat capacity is found to be $3Nk$. In other words, each dimension contributes Nk to the heat capacity. Therefore, $3Nk$ should be the heat capacity of all solids at sufficiently high temperatures.

If we take a mole of material, then $N = 6.023 \times 10^{23}$, Avogadro's number. The heat capacity is thus approximately 6 cal/mole/deg. If we now look up the heat capacity per mole of the elements (crystalline solids), we find all the room temperature values are close to the theoretical value of 6. Diamond is the sole exception. Although the reasons for this exception are no mystery, we will not delve into them here. They have to do with the fact that in diamond u/k is so large that the constant portion of the C_v versus temperature curve is shifted to much higher temperatures.

4

From Infinity
up to Zero

SUPPOSE WE WERE to start over, describing how hot an object is by its ǝɹnʇɐɹǝdɯǝʇ (pronounced *reciprocal of temperature*). We would choose this physical quantity—ǝɹnʇɐɹǝdɯǝʇ—in order to simplify the full range of its numerical scale. When we are dealing with ǝɹnʇɐɹǝdɯǝʇ, we find that a very cold object can have large numerical values for its ǝɹnʇɐɹǝdɯǝʇ. As the object becomes hotter, the numerical value of its ǝɹnʇɐɹǝdɯǝʇ goes down toward zero. Familiar situations, such as weather or fire or refrigeration, involve only a rather limited range of values for ǝɹnʇɐɹǝdɯǝʇ—from moderately large values to rather small ones.

However, there are some real situations in which objects become very hot and have a zero ǝɹnʇɐɹǝdɯǝʇ. There are even situations in which they become "hotter still" and have large negative values of ǝɹnʇɐɹǝdɯǝʇ. In this chapter we turn our vocabulary upside down and present a logical description of this unusual range in terms of the *absolute* temperature. We will also explore some interesting applications.

In the usual sense of temperature, *infinite* temperatures are impossible. So are *negative* temperatures, since they describe conditions even hotter than those corresponding to infinite temperatures. And yet, devices using situations accurately described by negative temperatures will be of increasing benefit to all of us during the next decade. The extent to which we are able to apply the negative temperatures attainable in solids, in liquids, and in gases challenges both our ingenuity and our understanding. To fully utilize the striking advantages of negative temperatures, it is necessary to understand them in principle as well as in practice.

What are the situations in which an infinite or a negative temperature makes sense? We will recognize quite a few cases as we explore the meaning of a temperature with a negative value.

To visualize the special requirements for a negative temperature, let's recall the discussion in Chapter Three of a temperature as a microscopic parameter. The temperature T of a given collection of N identical particles reflects the way in which the total stored energy is shared among them. (We will call an object a "particle" when its internal energy remains constant during the measurement.) However, the object's external energy, measured with respect to its surroundings, may change. For example, inside a darkened flask of cool helium gas, each helium atom acts like a particle. As such, each helium atom trades its external energy with the others, without any energy being swallowed up internally. However, there may be different situations in which the same helium atoms are pulled apart into separate entities by a process called *ionization*. A helium atom is said to be ionized when one of its electrons is liberated, leaving behind a helium *ion*— a helium nucleus with only one electron bound to it. In any situation involving ionization, it is clear that the helium atom is not behaving as a single particle.

A grain of ordinary table salt is another example of a collection of particles. Inside such a crystal of sodium chloride, we find sodium and chlorine nuclei arranged alternately in a simple cubic array. Each nucleus is considered to be a particle as long as it keeps its same internal properties. With constant internal nuclear energy, which implies constant mass, constant charge, constant spin, and constant shape, each sodium nucleus and each chlorine nucleus will behave as a particle.

Our concern, then, is the external energy of each of the particles. We assume that the particles are identical, but identifiable. By "identical" we mean—as we have in other chapters—having the same behavioral characteristics. Now, in our sample of N identical particles, each identifiable by its position, by its motion relative to the other particles, and by the rest of its external energy, we will often find conservation of the total of these particle energies although energy is exchanged between particles. Therefore, we want to count instantaneously the number of particles having each of the energy values possible for individual particles. Later we will show how this count can be taken using radiation, but for the time being we can assume that such a count has been completed many times, and we are interested in relating the results of our particle counts to the temperature of our sample.

Normally, in our collection of N particles, the average number found to have a given energy E_{upper} is related by the temperature T to the average number of those having the energy E_{lower} by the expression of Eq. 3.27, which can be written as

$$N_{upper} = N_{lower} \, e^{-\left[\frac{E_{upper} - E_{lower}}{kT}\right]}, \tag{4.1}$$

where e is the natural base of logarithms, and k is a positive number called *Boltzmann's constant*. As we mentioned earlier, k is the increase in energy per atom needed to raise the temperature of a monatomic ideal gas by one degree; k is found to have the value $1.38 \times (10^{-16})$ ergs per degree Kelvin.

Equation 4.1 tells us that T is a positive number when there are fewer particles with an upper energy, E_{upper}, than with a lower energy, E_{lower}. When the temperature goes higher it becomes more likely to find particles with greater energies.

We may see this relation between temperature and particle counts more easily by solving Eq. 4.1 for T, with this result:

$$T = \frac{E_{upper} - E_{lower}}{k(\log_e N_{lower} - \log_e N_{upper})} = \frac{E_{upper} - E_{lower}}{k \log_e \left(\frac{N_{lower}}{N_{upper}}\right)}. \tag{4.2}$$

Now as the N particles are given more and more energy to share, the ratio of the populations, $\dfrac{N_{lower}}{N_{upper}}$, decreases and T becomes a larger positive number.

In order to have T become infinite in Eq. 4.2, the denominator must go to zero, or the numerator must become infinite. The former would occur only if $N_{lower} = N_{upper}$. Since the two energies we selected were any two of the many possible energy levels, we see that all the energies from zero up to the largest possible particle energy must have equal populations for T to have the value of infinity. Now, each of the two energy values as defined for Eq. 4.2 includes the kinetic energy of motion of the particles. We note that the kinetic energy of a particle has no limiting value (short of the value at which the particle comes apart and the quantities in the equation no longer apply). Therefore, the energy values possible for a single particle (called *energy levels,* for short) have no upper limit. This is indicated schematically in the diagram of Fig. 4.1. With ever higher energies possible for each particle, it is *not* possible to have *all* the N's equal and still keep the sample together. Therefore, an infinite value for T is not possible in the former case of Eq. 4.2.

Figure 4.1 Observable amounts (*levels*) of kinetic energy for a particle confined in a rigid box.

In the latter case, an infinite value for E_{upper} would take an infinite amount of energy to increase N_{upper} from zero to one particle. In fact, most particles break up and are no longer single particles at high but measurable kinetic energies. In any case, it is quite impossible to put any real object at an infinite temperature when the temperature value relates the populations of all the possible energies of the individual particles contained in that object.

What about negative temperatures? With the energy difference in the numerator of Eq. 4.2 defined as a positive quantity, a negative value of T could arise only from every N_{upper} being larger than any N_{lower}. Such an upside-down count of the particles would be impossible to find, for the same reasons as those given above in discussing infinite temperatures. Therefore, negative temperatures are impossible in the same sense that infinite temperatures are—only more so.

Before we proceed to the exciting challenges of practical negative temperatures, we ought to be able to find a situation in which negative temperatures are theoretically possible. Where can we put a reasonable restriction on the definitions involved in the basic Eqs. 4.1 and 4.2? The specification of energies is a good place to try.

Energy is a many-faceted physical quantity. It appears in a variety of forms, as mentioned earlier, and in some of its forms the amount of energy depends on the set of coordinates (frame of reference) used for measurement. *Kinetic energy* is used to describe motions of one or more particles, such as free flight, or rotation, or vibration. *Potential energy* is used to describe the energy stored in the combination of one or more particles, and an "external" force field acting on them. For examples, we could take the stored energy of electrons in an electric field, or of nuclei in a gravitational field, or of nuclei (or electrons) spinning and therefore precessing in an external magnetic field.

One of energy's intriguing features is that a given particle may keep distinct values of each of several energy forms for long periods of time. An example that shows this separation and separate conservation is the collection of identical particles, described as nuclei, at the lattice points in a single crystal of an ionic solid, such as sodium 23 (written Na^{23}) in sodium chloride. There are three forms of energy of the nuclei that are quite easily separable. Each nucleus is in a certain state of aggregation, and therefore the value of nuclear energy stored in the first excited state of the nucleus is a large amount above the ground state. This energy jump is usually at least a billion times the thermal energies of the nuclei in the crystal. Hence, the nucleus stays in the lowest (nuclear) energy level, independent of its thermal motions in the crystal. Furthermore, each nucleus vibrates around its average position (lattice point) in the crystal. Usually a core of tightly bound electrons sticks with the nucleus during the vibrations, and the effective particle for vibrational energy is an ion of much smaller charge than a bare nucleus. During these vibrations, the kinetic energy of the ion, as it passes through its lattice point, is converted into electrostatic energy of position when it reaches its peak amplitude. Packets of this vibrational energy are called *phonons*. A third form of energy for individual nuclei (or ions) is their *magnetic* or *spin energy* in an external magnetic field.

Now, the energy levels available to such an ion, vibrating in consort with its neighbors, are very close together in a crystal of any reasonable size. In a grain of table salt, for instance, the 10^{21} vibrational energy levels are crowded into a very small energy spread, about equal to the energy required to lift an invisible speck of dust just a few inches in the earth's gravitational field. Yet the magnetic energy of such nuclei remains separated (and thereby conserved) from their vibrational energy for periods of time as long as hours, in many cases. It is this conservation of one form of energy for long periods of time that leads to useful restrictions on energy specifications for Eqs. 4.1 and 4.2.

A word about spin and the magnetic energy associated with spin seems in order here. Let's look at nuclear magnetism, for example. Each nucleus of the *isotope* of sodium, called Na^{23}, has closely the mass of 23 protons, but its charge is only that of 11 protons. Hence, we presume the remainder of the mass to be in neutrons. Nuclei of the other sodium isotopes have the same electric charge, but differ in mass by one or more neutrons. Every nucleus has among its characteristic properties for its nuclear ground state a certain constant amount of angular momentum associated with the motions of its neutrons or protons, labeled

$$\frac{h}{2\pi}\sqrt{I(I+1)}.$$

The number h is a universal constant of action, called Planck's constant, and is observed to be about $6.6(10^{-27})$ erg seconds. The number I is specific to each isotope, and is observed to be either zero, a positive integer, or a positive half-integer. Each Na^{23} nucleus has a spin number of $I = 3/2$ and therefore a constant angular momentum of $(h/2\pi)\sqrt{15/4}$.

A moving charge displays an associated magnetic field. A rotating charge of finite dimensions displays the magnetic field of a small bar magnet or magnetic dipole. The axis of rotation lies along the direction of the effective dipole, as illustrated in Fig. 4.2. Every rotating nuclear charge, such as Na^{23}, shows a constant value for its spin number I. Therefore, whatever energy is associated with the kinetic energy of spinning is internal to the nucleus and will not concern us here.

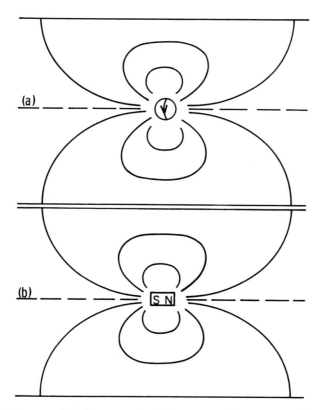

Figure 4.2 Diagram of similar magnetic fields generated by spinning electric charge (a), and by permanent bar magnet (b).

However, when we bring up another magnetic field from outside that nucleus, the spinning nucleus has an external energy of position due to its *dipole moment* μ, just as a permanent bar magnet does. In an "external" magnetic field H, this magnetic energy of position, called *Zeeman energy*, is written

$$E_m = \mu H \cos \theta, \tag{4.3}$$

where θ is the angle between H and μ, and μ is the dipole moment arising from the spinning charge. The proportionality of μ to the spin angular momentum may be expressed in terms of the gyromagnetic ratio γ as

$$\mu = \gamma h \sqrt{I(I + 1)}. \tag{4.4}$$

Hence, we may use any two of the numbers I, μ, and γ to characterize a given nucleus. Usually we use I and γ. For example, sodium 23 has $I = 3/2$ and $\gamma = 1{,}126.2$ cycles per second per gauss.

The magnetic or Zeeman energy is stored in each spinning nucleus as the field is raised from 0 to H. In a strong applied field H, each nucleus can take on only discrete values of its Zeeman energy. These values are given by

$$E_m = \mu H \frac{m_I}{\sqrt{I(I + 1)}} = m_I \gamma h H, \tag{4.5}$$

where m_I can have only the values I, $(I - 1), \ldots, (-I + 1)$, or $-I$. We often interpret this quantization of allowed energy in terms of a *vector model* in which there is precession of the spin around the direction of H at constant angle θ and at the constant frequency of γH. This model is sketched in Fig. 4.3, showing the angle θ, given by the expression $\cos \theta = m_I / \sqrt{I(I + 1)}$.

Changes in the magnetic or Zeeman energy of a given isolated nucleus occur only by changes in the applied H or changes in the value of m_I. The smallest change possible in m_I is 1, and m_I is called a *quantum number*.

We can see that the Zeeman energy does not depend on the other external coordinates of the nucleus. Therefore, this form of energy for the particle is separable from the other forms of energy a given particle can have. In many real situations, the Zeeman energy of nuclei is separately conserved for hours.

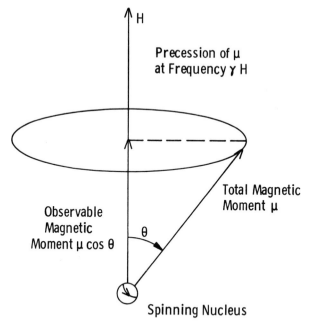

Figure 4.3 Vector model showing uniform precession.

The above discussion of Zeeman energy and the following one of spin energy applies equally well to unpaired electrons with I being replaced by the electronic spin number S. The separation and conservation of Zeeman energy will be seen to apply to single, unpaired electrons in some cases as well.

In weak or zero external fields, the magnetic energy of a collection of spinning particles is not zero. Each individual particle "sees" the local magnetic field due to the magnetic moments of its neighbors. Visualize, for example, an extension of Fig. 4.1 including many dipoles spaced reasonably far apart. The magnetic field at a large distance r_i from a dipole of moment μ_i appears as a *local field* with the value $H_{\text{dipole}} = \dfrac{\mu_i}{r_i^3} F(\theta)$, where $F(\theta)$ is a numerical factor varying from 2 to 0 as the angle θ_i between $\bar{\mu}_i$ and $\bar{\mu}$ varies from 0 to $\pi/2$. The magnetic energy of the one particle in the fields of all the other particles is that of a sum written as

$$E_{\text{local}} = \mu \sum_i \frac{\mu_i}{r_i^3} F(\theta) \cos \theta_i, \qquad (4.6)$$

where each θ_i varies in time according to the precession of the neighboring spin at distance r_i.

When this local energy is large, the magnetic energy is not separable from the other forms of energy that depend on position (r). Rather, we find cooperation between spins that often takes on remarkable appearances. Large local fields between electron spins anchored at each iron atom (actually, more precisely, each iron ion) give rise to the ferromagnetism of metallic iron and to the ferrimagnetism of the iron oxides.

When the local energy is small, it serves as a means by which Zeeman energy is transferred between spins in the various parts of a sample. The process of such transfer may be pictured in terms of a pair of spins far enough apart so that each E_{local} is very much smaller than E_{Zeeman} but close enough so that the precessional variations in their E_{local}'s occasionally cause the pair to flip together, each changing their quantum numbers by 1, one by $+1$ and the other by -1. The net effect of such a double spin flip is to leave the total Zeeman energy unchanged, the total of E_{local}'s essentially unchanged, and the location of the stored Zeeman energy changed from one spin to the other.

Small values of the local energy are obtained, according to Eq. 4.6, either by small values of μ_i or by large values of r_i, or both. Our sample of sodium chloride, NaCl, illustrates the case of small μ_i. The interatomic distance in a crystal of NaCl is about 2 Angstroms or $2(10^{-8})$ centimeters. For $r_i = 2\text{Å}$, H_{local} is about one gauss. More distant neighbors generate much weaker fields because of larger r_i. So when the salt crystal is in an external field of thousands of gauss, the local fields are small, serving primarily to permit the diffusion of Zeeman energy throughout the crystal, while the total Zeeman energy is conserved. In this chapter, we will concern ourselves only with cases having weak local fields, and therefore the Zeeman energy of the particles is separable from other external energies and is capable of being conserved in the presence of a constant external magnetic field.

In summary, we see that the total energy available to a nucleus is an almost continuous set of values. However, as long as one form of its energy remains conserved (does not exchange with other forms), that energy can be listed separately. Lack of conservation of spin energy would occur, for example, when one nucleus changes its precessional angle θ and converts Zeeman energy to vibrational energy. As long as this lack of conservation occurs only occasionally for each particle, we can still list separately each set of energy levels (for the several forms of energy per particle).

What does separate listing of energy do to the meaning and to the value of temperature? Eq. 4.1 still holds for our box (or crystal) of nuclei. We may list energies separately as follows:

$$E_{\text{upper}} = E(\text{vibrational})_{\text{upper}} + E(\text{spin})_{\text{upper}}$$
$$E_{\text{lower}} = E(\text{vibrational})_{\text{lower}} + E(\text{spin})_{\text{lower}} \tag{4.7}$$

To specify the temperature by Eq. 4.2, we need only take the difference.

We can select any pair of energy levels, according to the unrestricted form of Eq. 4.2. The condition of conservation of one form of the energy allows us to restrict Eq. 4.2 to pairs of energy levels differing only in energy of that conserved form. For example, we might choose the pair of levels indicated in Eq. 4.7 to be different only by some vibrational energy of the crystal. The energy difference for Eq. 4.2 would then involve only vibrational energy of the lattice. Our particle counting, therefore, would give a ratio of N_{upper} to N_{lower} involving only vibrational excitation and from the ratio a temperature T equal to the normal temperature of the crystal, as indicated on the thermometer in contact with the crystal lattice. This temperature might well be termed the *lattice temperature,* since it is derived from considerations of the vibrational energy of the lattice, without taking notice of the other forms of energy of the same particles.

We could, on the other hand, choose the energies in Eq. 4.7 to differ only in magnetic energy of spin orientation. Suppose with a large field H being applied to the salt crystal, we select the pair of energy levels to be

$$E(\text{spin})_{\text{upper}} = m_I \gamma h H$$
and
$$E(\text{spin})_{\text{lower}} = (m_I - 1)\gamma h H. \tag{4.8}$$

Then the energy difference would be $E_{\text{upper}} - E_{\text{lower}} = \gamma h H$ and the particle count would give the *spin temperature, T_s,* as

$$T_s = \frac{\gamma h H}{k \log_e \dfrac{(N_{\text{lower}})}{(N_{\text{upper}})}}. \tag{4.9}$$

The spin temperature T_s is usually a number equal to the lattice temperature T. Certainly if we sample both temperatures periodically and find that they are both remaining constant with time, we usually expect to be looking at the equilibrium condition, with equal temperatures. (An important exception to this, with $T_s \neq T$, will be brought out in the discussion of the microwave maser.) If the particle count gives changing T_s, then we usually find T_s approaching T. This approach to equilibrium is called *relaxation* and will be discussed later, when we investigate an example of electrons that remain out of equilibrium for hours.

The existence of different temperatures in the same physical volume is one intriguing consequence of the conservation of separate forms of energy over reasonable periods of time. We have just discussed the case of a grain of salt in which the vibrational motion was described by the lattice temperature, equal to the usual temperature of the surroundings, and the spin temperature of the nuclei could be different from the lattice temperature. All this inside a single grain of salt! With separable forms of energy separately conserved, a collection of particles occupying a given space can be described by separate values of temperature. These values are often not equal in situations considered to be in "equilibrium."

There are other examples of separable energy forms that are of interest to negative temperatures. They include the magnetic (Zeeman) energy of paramagnetic ions or paramagnetic centers in crystals, and the electrostatic energy stored in luminescent centers. Each will be cited later in a practical example.

By now we have seen that for particles with separable forms of energy, we can find the parameter T for the energy levels of just one form, provided the total energy (in that form) of all the particles remains conserved for a reasonably long period of time. During this period of conservation, the parameter T will have the usual meaning of temperature, provided the particles reach the most probable distribution among the energy levels of this form of energy (e.g., Zeeman energy). To reach the most probable distribution, the particles must be able to exchange energy of the form in question rapidly among themselves—rapidly compared to the period of time during which that form of energy is conserved. The special temperature, such as spin temperature, then serves all the functions of temperature discussed in other chapters.

We note here that complete thermal isolation of our N particles is desired for the most leisurely, and hopefully the most accurate, speci- fication of temperature. However, complete thermal isolation of the particles, that is, the grain of salt, is not possible; there will always remain a finite heat leak to the surroundings. Neither is it possible to completely isolate one form of the particles' external energy from another form; there will always remain a finite leak to the other forms of energy. To refer to the ideal case in which we imagine zero heat leak of either kind, we will put our particles in a box with perfectly rigid walls. But in searching for a real situation capable of sustaining infinite or negative temperatures, we must admit the existence of finite, though small, heat leaks.

Returning to our search for a physical situation in which T can take on negative values, we make use of the separate listing of energy levels. To avoid the previous objection of needing an infinite supply of energy, we need have only an upper limit for the energy levels availa- ble to our N trapped particles. With a definite upper limit to the energy (in this form) available to each particle, only a finite amount is required to put the particles into an upside-down distribution. For such a distribution to be the most probable one, the temperature parameter has to have a *negative* value in Eq. 4.2. This distribution is called *inverted*. An amount of energy no greater than N times the energy of the uppermost level is needed to put the N particles into an inverted distribution. Keeping the inverted distribution in the face of ever-present relaxation is always a challenge for any practical application.

An upper limit is present in many forms of energy, especially if we restrict the size of the energy increments (quanta) that we inject into our box of particles. Several examples come to mind. The magnetic energy of spin orientation of each spinning particle has $2I + 1$ values in a constant field H. The four values for a nucleus of $I = 3/2$ are illustrated in Fig. 4.4. The maximum value of the Zeeman energy in a given H occurs for $m_I = I$. In every one of the other possible orien- tations (values of θ in Fig. 4.3), the particle has less Zeeman energy. Therefore, we expect that spinning particles can be put into an inverted distribution with regard to their Zeeman energy levels.

Another example might be the kinetic energy of the mobile electrons that help to "glue" a crystal together. There is a gap in the possible energy values, when the motion of such an electron through the crystal will permit strong reflections due to the periodicity of the lattice. An illustration of the energy levels can be seen in Fig. 4.5 and Fig. 4.8. An electron, moving with energy just below such a gap, cannot receive small increments of kinetic energy; it needs to be given an amount greater than the energy gap in order to have its kinetic energy increased. An additional source of quantization of the kinetic energy of such an electron is its cyclotron motion in a strong magnetic field. However, electrons in this situation usually share their kinetic energy very quickly with the vibrating lattice. Recently, samples of sufficient purity have been prepared to allow such electrons to conserve their kinetic energy unto themselves for as long as microseconds at very low temperatures. When this time is made long enough, we should see many fascinating developments involving distributions of electrons that conserve their kinetic energy separately from lattice phonons.

Another very common example of particles having large gaps in their energy level spectrum are the atoms, molecules, and ions that luminesce. The optical energy they give up by luminescing is itself a direct measure of one of the gaps. There are usually others of comparable size. Discussion of conservation of this form of electrostatic energy is difficult, because the excited atoms usually do not interact between themselves. One measure of the period of conservation is the lifetime of the atom in its excited state, occasionally as long as one second.

Before we seek out some of the striking successes recently attained

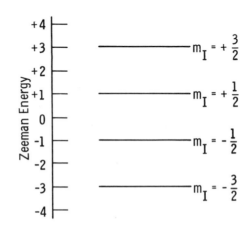

Figure 4.4 Observable Zeeman energy levels for a nucleus in a strong magnetic field, H. Four levels are shown for $I = 3/2$. Energy scale is in units of $\gamma_I hH$ for positive γ_I.

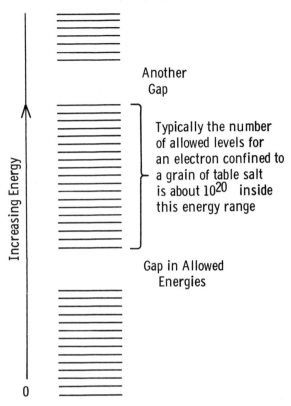

Increasing Energy

0

Another
Gap

Typically the number
of allowed levels for
an electron confined to
a grain of table salt
is about 10^{20} inside
this energy range

Gap in Allowed
Energies

Figure 4.5 Observable levels of kinetic energy of a particle in periodic potential in a rigid box. Gaps indicate schematically the effect of the periodic potential on the allowed motion.

in the practical art of obtaining inverted distributions, let's calculate the most probable distribution of N particles among a limited set of energy levels, limited in number for ease of counting and limited in energy with a large gap above them to make possible an inverted distribution. Comparison of the result for four levels—essentially the general case—with that for two levels will illustrate the utility of the temperature concept.

THE GENERAL CASE FOR INFINITE AND
NEGATIVE TEMPERATURES

We repeat here some of the discussion in Chapter Three of the statistical arrangements of a large number (N) of particles among the allowed energy levels. However, we add the restriction that all N particles are to be found having individual energies no greater than a fixed value E_U. For ease of counting, let's consider the case where each particle can have one of only four values of the particular form of energy under consideration. The case of four levels has all the generality of any larger number. By listing the levels of only one form of energy, we can surely be talking about a real situation when we speak of only four levels containing all N particles below a large energy gap.

The extreme distributions are of special interest. If the particles have zero energy, they are all in the lowest level, and they may be said to have a temperature of zero, just as explained in Chapter Three. As their stored energy is increased, their temperature rises. The maximum amount of stored energy possible is N times the energy E_U; for this, all N are in the uppermost level, and their temperature is zero again, according to Eq. 4.2.

Before we trace the temperature as it goes from zero to zero, we should add the possibility of heat flow through the walls of the box, and note the direction of heat flow for each extreme. When heat can flow through the walls, and contact is made to any other collection not at these extremes, heat will flow inward, for the extreme $T = 0$ with stored energy of 0. The flow is inward, because there is no internal energy available to flow out. Therefore, this extreme, $T = 0$ with stored energy of 0, is very cold; as a few of the particles receive the incoming energy and populate one of the upper three levels, the temperature corresponds to the usual case of very low temperatures, which will be discussed in detail later.

On the other hand, the extreme $T = 0$, with stored energy NE_U, could not receive any more energy and have all N particles remain below the gap. Therefore, when heat flow is allowed with another collection not at this extreme, the heat flow must be outward, and we conclude that this extreme of $T = 0$, with maximum stored energy, is *very hot*. After a few quanta of energy have leaked out, a few of the particles will be in the lower three levels, and the temperature will have a small negative value; this collection of particles will still be much hotter than any normal surroundings. Thus it is a general characteristic of any real situation described by a negative temperature to be hotter than its surroundings, and therefore to give up heat to every part of the surroundings with which it has contact. This is an unstable situation, and either the temperature will change from its low negative value as the stored energy leaks out, or we must somehow inject energy into the particles in a special way, called *pumping*, in order to maintain the very hot condition of negative temperature, despite the unavoidable outflow.

The quantitative behavior of our isolated box of N identical particles can be seen from a few examples. We want, first, to apply the expression, developed in Chapter Three, for the number of arrangements in a particular distribution, or the number of ways of obtaining it (designated by ω). We write for the distribution, N_1 in the lowest level, N_2 in the second, . . . , N_u in the uppermost, that

$$\omega = \frac{N!}{N_1!\, N_2! \ldots N_u}. \tag{4.10}$$

For four levels, the expression we will use is

$$\omega = N!/(N_1!\, N_2!\, N_3!\, N_4!), \tag{4.11}$$

where N factorial, $N!$, is the usual abbreviation for the product $N(N-1)(N-2)\ldots(2)(1)$.

For an understanding of the expression of Eq. 4.11, it will be helpful to digress from the case of large N where a temperature can be meaningful to the case of small N where we can enumerate the probability ω for all the possible distributions. The analysis for $N = 4$ is given in Fig. 4.6, where the levels have been chosen to be equally spaced for convenience. Each of the possible distributions is graphed in the second column of Fig. 4.6, corresponding to the value of stored energy listed in the first column. The most probable distribution (largest value of ω) for a given stored energy is clearly the most spread-out one. If we assume that the four particles exchange energy among themselves during the time that any one value of stored energy is conserved (isolated box), then the average populations of the four levels would be those listed in the last column. The trend of populations with stored energy is apparent; approximately equal populations correspond to the stored energy at half its maximum value, and all in the uppermost level, to the maximum stored energy.

Now we are ready to look at a case with large N. In Chapter Three we showed that the most probable distribution of a large number of particles among an unlimited set of energy levels gave rise to a unique

Stored Energy	Possible Distributions	Number of Ways Each Distribution Can Be Obtained	Average Populations Expected
$E = 0$		$w = 1$	$N_4 = N_3 = 0$ $N_2 = 0$ $N_1 = 4$
$E = S$		$w = 4$	$N_4 = N_3 = 0$ $N_2 = 1$ $N_1 = 3$
$E = 2S$	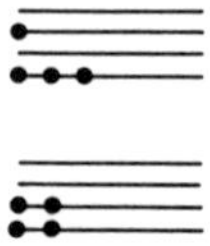	$w = 4$ $w = \dfrac{4!}{2!2!} = 6$	$N_4 = 0$ $N_3 = 4/10$ $N_2 = 12/10$ $N_1 = 24/10$
$E = 3S$	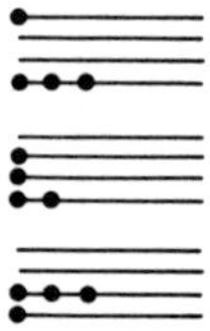	$w = 4$ $w = \dfrac{4!}{1!1!2!} = 12$ $w = \dfrac{4!}{3!1!} = 4$	$N_4 = 4/20$ $N_3 = 12/20$ $N_2 = 24/20$ $N_1 = 36/20$
$E = 4S$	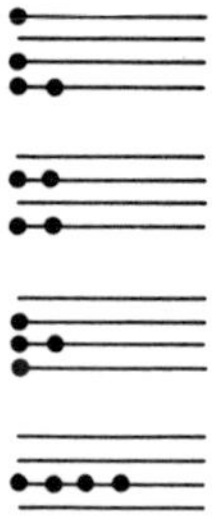	$w = \dfrac{4!}{1!1!2!} = 12$ $w = \dfrac{4!}{2!2!} = 6$ $w = \dfrac{4!}{1!2!1!} = 12$ $w = \dfrac{4!}{4!} = 1$	$N_4 = 12/31$ $N_3 = 24/31$ $N_2 = 40/31$ $N_1 = 48/31$
$E = 5S$	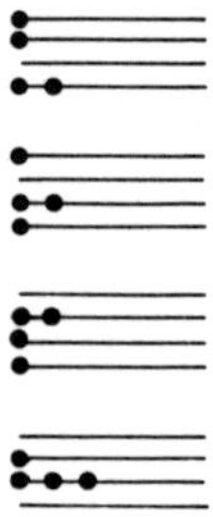	$w = \dfrac{4!}{1!1!2!} = 12$ $w = \dfrac{4!}{1!2!1!} = 12$ $w = \dfrac{4!}{2!1!1!} = 12$ $w = \dfrac{4!}{1!3!} = 4$	$N_4 = 24/40$ $N_3 = 40/40$ $N_2 = 48/40$ $N_1 = 48/40$

Figure 4.6

Stored Energy	Possible Distributions	Number of Ways Each Distribution Can Be Obtained	Average Populations Expected
E = 6S		$w = \dfrac{4!}{2!\,2!} = 6$ $w = \dfrac{4!}{1!\,1!\,1!\,1!} = 24$ $w = \dfrac{4!}{3!\,1!} = 4$ $w = \dfrac{4!}{3!\,1!} = 4$ $w = \dfrac{4!}{2!\,2!} = 6$	$N_4 = 40/44$ $N_3 = 48/44$ $N_2 = 48/44$ $N_1 = 40/44$
E = 7S		as for E = 5S	$N_4 = 48/40$ $N_3 = 48/40$ $N_2 = 40/40$ $N_1 = 24/40$
E = 8S	Each Upside Down from E=4S	as for E = 4S	$N_4 = 48/31$ $N_3 = 40/31$ $N_2 = 24/31$ $N_1 = 12/31$
E = 9S	Each Upside Down from E = 3S	as for E = 3S	$N_4 = 36/20$ $N_3 = 24/20$ $N_2 = 12/20$ $N_1 = 4/20$
E = 10S		as for E = 2S	$N_4 = 24/10$ $N_3 = 12/10$ $N_2 = 4/10$ $N_1 = 0$
E = 11S		$w = \dfrac{4!}{3!\,1!} = 4$	$N_4 = 3$ $N_3 = 1$ $N_2 = N_1 = 0$
E = 12S		$w = \dfrac{4!}{4!} = 1$	$N_4 = 0$ $N_3 = N_2 = N_1 = 0$

temperature parameter. Here we will show that a similar relation applies when the large number of particles are confined to only four energy levels. In addition, we will show how accurately the most probable distribution is *the* most probable.

In most real situations, N will be a very large number (10^{10} or more). For large N, the enumeration shown in Fig. 4.6 is quite lengthy even with just four levels. Any ambitious soul is urged to enumerate the case of $N = 20$, before tackling $N = 10^{20}$. Fortunately, however, the distribution having the maximum value of ω can be identified rather readily, without such tabulation. We use the idea that a maximum value is slightly larger than its neighboring values, for small changes in distribution. To tell if the particle distribution, N_1, N_2, N_3, N_4, is the most probable one, we compare its probability (ω from Eq. 4.11) with those for a pair of the nearest distributions, which are consistent with the same value of stored energy, namely, the distributions:

$$N_1 - 1, N_2 + 2, N_3 - 1, N_4$$
and
$$N_1 + 1, N_2 - 2, N_3 + 1, N_4.$$

Writing ω' for the first, and ω'' for the second, the comparison gives

$$\frac{\omega'}{\omega} = \frac{N_1 N_3}{(N_2 + 2)(N_2 + 1)} = \frac{N_1 N_3}{N_2{}^2}\left(1 - \frac{3}{N_2}\right)$$

and

$$\frac{\omega''}{\omega} = \frac{N_2(N_2 - 1)}{(N_1 + 1)(N_3 + 1)} = \frac{N_2{}^2}{N_1 N_3}\left(1 - \frac{1}{N_1} - \frac{1}{N_2} - \frac{1}{N_3}\right). \tag{4.12}$$

Now ω is a maximum only if both ω'/ω and ω''/ω are less than unity. Therefore, ω is a maximum only when

$$N_1 N_3 = N_2{}^2 \tag{4.13}$$

more closely than a factor of $(1 - 3/N_2)$. This is the same condition for the most probable distribution as developed in the earlier chapter for an unlimited set, namely

$$\frac{N_1}{N_2} = \frac{N_2}{N_3} = \frac{N_3}{N_4}. \tag{4.14}$$

The last equality is included because the same analysis applies to a change in distribution involving levels 2, 3, and 4. Furthermore, it is apparent from the expression for ω (Eq. 4.11) that there is only one maximum for ω under conditions of constant N and constant stored energy.

Thus, we conclude that the most probable distribution of a large number of identical particles among equally spaced energy levels, below a large energy gap, is the one with a constant ratio between the populations of adjacent levels. The ratio can be used to define the temperature by the expression

$$T = \frac{S}{k \log_e \left(\dfrac{N_1}{N_2}\right)}, \qquad (4.15)$$

where S is the energy spacing. This expression for the temperature T applies in general, when S is the difference in energy $E_2 - E_1$. Therefore, T becomes negative when the upper level has the larger population.

Another example using the four equally spaced levels and a large value number of particles will confirm the range and the precision of the temperature values. A few distributions for $N = 4(10^{10})$ are listed in Table 4.A, together with the temperatures to be associated with them under conditions of constant stored energy E, and rapid internal exchange. The second line gives the distribution for a temperature of boiling liquid helium, for S equal to the energy in a *microwave photon*.

TABLE 4.A

Stored energy E	Most probable distribution				Corresponding temperature T
	N_1	N_2	N_3	N_4	
(units of 10^{10} S)	(units of 10^{10} particles)				
0	4.00	0	0	0	0
5.48	1.16	1.05	0.94	0.85	$+10\ S/k$
5.89	1.03	1.01	0.99	0.97	$+50\ S/k$
5.99	1.0025	1.0008	0.9992	0.9975	$+600\ S/k$
6.00	1.0000	1.0000	1.0000	1.0000	infinity
6.01	0.9975	0.9992	1.0008	1.0025	$-600\ S/k$
6.10	0.97	0.99	1.01	1.03	$-50\ S/k$
6.52	0.85	0.94	1.05	1.16	$-10\ S/k$
12.00	0	0	0	4.00	0
(the maximum)					

Most probable distributions of $4(10^{10})$ particles among four energy levels, spaced S energy units apart, for selected values of the stored energy.

The third line, with 9 percent more stored energy, shows the temperature up to $+50$ S/k; the fourth, up to $+600$ S/k, or room temperature, for S in the microwave range.

The stored energy of just one half the maximum (fifth line in Table 4.A) gives the most probable distribution of $N_1 = N_2 = N_3 = N_4$ to an accuracy of a few parts in 10^{10}. The associated temperature is as precisely infinite as the concept of temperature is precise. Actually, thermal insulation or some other experimental condition will always present a much coarser limit than this in such a hot situation.

Negative temperatures are also shown in Table 4.A. For example, when the population of any level is 2 percent larger than the level below it, the temperature is the negative of a temperature below the boiling point of air (for S in microwave range), and represents a very hot situation indeed.

In summary, the general case for a bona fide negative (or infinite) temperature rests on there being a large number of identical, trapped particles,

> whose energy is separable into several forms,
> whose total energy in one form is conserved for periods of time long compared to the time required for exchanging that form of energy among the particles, and
> whose energy levels for that conserved form of energy have a definite upper limit.

This special temperature has then the same dependence on the population distribution (Eq. 4.15) as for the normal case of open-ended energy levels (Eq. 4.2).

We noted that as more energy was slowly added, the temperature rose continuously up through large positive values, infinity, and larger negative values, to small negative values. We also saw that for most of this range our particles were very much hotter than their surroundings, as far as the one conserved form of energy was concerned.

It takes a bit of explanation to assure ourselves that in a real situation energy can be so well stored as to permit negative temperatures, especially if this involves finding the same particles with part of their energy (one form) so well stored, and the rest so well blended. The storage of chemical energy is familiar, but somehow the fact of rapid exchange between particles makes the isolation required for negative temperatures more unusual. It will be easier if we concern ourselves with just two levels, at first, until we have looked at several examples. In the event that there is anything special about the case of two levels, we will review it before discussing practical cases and the problems of pumping.

TWO LEVELS ALL ALONE

Suppose we select, as a sample to keep in mind while discussing the two-level case, the unpaired electrons scattered sparsely throughout a cubic lattice of potassium chloride (KCl, for short) but each anchored at a vacant lattice point, where a chlorine negative ion would be if the lattice were perfect. An electron, so trapped, is called an *F-center*. Each such electron has a spin angular momentum, with a spin number of $s = \frac{1}{2}$, in its lowest level of electrostatic energy. Therefore, each F-center in the applied field H has two possible orientations of its magnetic moment and just two spin energy levels separated by an amount

$$E_2 - E_1 = \gamma_s hH. \tag{4.16}$$

The first excited level of an F-center is quite high (about two electron volts) but its detailed structure is not yet known. In equilibrium, with lattice temperatures as high as room temperature, all F-centers are in the two lowest (spin) levels. The levels are indicated in Fig. 4.7 with the populations to be expected when their spin energy is in equilibrium with their lattice energy at the boiling point of helium, 4.2°K. Incidentally, we will see that to get close to such equilibrium may take hours.

Now, we want to look at the relation of spin populations to stored energy and to spin temperature. A tabulation, as in Table 4.B, shows that normal spin temperatures correspond to a slight excess of spins in the lower level. The 5 percent excess on the second line in Table 4.B, giving $T_s = +10 \, S/k$, is closely the condition pictured for F-centers at 4.2°K in Fig. 4.7, with about 47.5 percent of the maximum possible stored energy. As the stored energy is increased slowly, the spin temperature goes up through infinity to negative values, with the same formal relation to N_1 and N_2 as in the general case (Eq. 4.15). Three values of negative spin temperature are illustrated in the lower

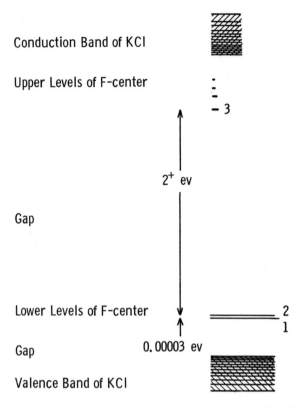

Conduction Band of KCl

Upper Levels of F-center

— 3

2^+ ev

Gap

Lower Levels of F-center _____ 2
_____ 1

Gap   0. 00003 ev

Valence Band of KCl

Figure 4.7 Energy levels for F-centers in a crystal of potassium chloride. Populations are $N_1/N_2 = 1.11$ and $N_3 = 0.00$ for equilibrium at 4.2°K and 3200 oersteds.

half of Table 4.B. The next to the last line shows the distribution for 52.5 percent of $E_{maximum}$ having the temperature of -10 S/k, a negative temperature corresponding to $-4.2°$K and to the inverse of the distribution for the F-centers in Table 4.A.

Thus, we find that the way a given number of particles populate just two energy levels can be described by a special temperature, for example, spin temperature. This special temperature can have values from zero up through the value of infinity to negative ones and finally up to zero.

An interesting question can be raised about counting the particles without disturbing such special temperatures. First, however, we should note a significant difference between the two-level case and the four-level or general case. For particles confined to four levels the

TABLE 4.B

Stored energy E	The only distribution		Excess in lower level $\dfrac{N_1 - N_2}{N}$	Corresponding temperature T
	N_1	N_2		
0	2.00	0	100%	0
0.95	1.05	0.95	5%	$+10\ S/k$
0.99	1.01	0.99	1%	$+50\ S/k$
0.9991	1.0009	0.9991	0.08%	$+600\ S/k$
1.0000	1.0000	1.0000	none	infinity
1.0009	0.9991	1.0009	-0.08%	$-600\ S/k$
1.01	0.99	1.01	-1%	$-50\ S/k$
1.05	0.95	1.05	-5%	$-10\ S/k$
2.00 (the maximum)	0	2.00	-100%	0

Temperature for N particles in just two levels, separated by S energy units. N is chosen to be $2(10^{10})$ for convenience. E is given in units of $10^{10}\ S$; N_1 and N_2, in units of 10^{10}.

existence of a single temperature means the particles are arranged in *the* most probable distribution. Interaction between the particles is usually required in order to obtain the most probable distribution. For particles confined to two levels, the temperature parameter is uniquely determined by the stored energy; there is only one possible distribution and one value of T for a given E. In fact, a special temperature can be assigned to a collection of isolated particles which are confined to the same two energy levels but do not interact with each other. For example, negative temperatures have been apt descriptions of the ammonia molecules in the beam of the ammonia clock as well as of the dilute luminescent centers in some phosphors, and in laser light sources.

Now we return to the problem of counting particles in order to check the relations between temperature and populations such as Eqs. 4.2 and 4.15. Several methods have been used. The particles themselves have been counted in some of the elegant molecular beam experiments at such places as Columbia University. The most popular techniques for "counting" populations, however, use electromagnetic radiation of variable frequency as a probe. They obtain the particle count from the change in the radiation transmitted, or reflected, by the sample.

We picture the process of counting in the following rather simple but effective manner. We know that:

(1) A beam of electromagnetic energy behaves in some ways as if it, too, is a collection of identical particles, called *photons*.

(2) Each photon of frequency f contains an amount of energy equal to hf, where h is Planck's constant. The quanta of energy stored in the oscillating electromagnetic fields and moving with the velocity of light are exchanged as individuals when energy is lost from a beam of photons either by absorption or by scattering. A few comparison numbers may be of interest: hf is so small for f in the audio frequency range (10^3 cycles per second) that quantum effects are extremely difficult to observe and adding one such quantum of energy to every particle in any object would increase the temperature by only ten micromicrodegrees Kelvin; hf is still very small for f in the radar or microwave range (10^{10} cycles per second) corresponding to an increase of one-quarter of a degree Kelvin; but hf is large enough for f in the visible light region (10^{15} cycles per second) to give rise to many quantum effects, such as photoemission of electrons from a metal surface and luminescence of sharp lines—nearly monochromatic light.

(3) There is often found to be a *resonance* between a beam of electromagnetic energy and a collection of particles, when the energy of individual photons, hf, is just equal to the separation S in the energy levels of the (individual) particles. In other words, the energy condition for resonance can be written

$$hf = S. \tag{4.17}$$

The resonance condition is clearly an energy quantum effect, yet it has analogous classical conditions. For example, the resonance condition corresponds to the usual frequency at which a small child on a rope swing needs to be pushed.

We now set out to count the particles distributed as N_1 and N_2 in the two levels, by sending resonance radiation through a thin sample and observing the ratio of the number of photons incident, n_i, to the number transmitted, n_t. We note that the total energy is conserved when a photon is absorbed out of the beam into the particles, because the transmitted beam has one less photon, and the particles have additional energy equal to hf. This absorption process is forced or *stimulated* by the presence of the electromagnetic forces due to the photons themselves. Watching one particle in the lower level as n_i resonant photons pass by every second, we would eventually find that the particle had jumped to the upper level by absorbing one photon. The process of stimulated absorption occurs by purely random chance; so the total chance of the particle making such a jump in one second is proportional to the number of chances (photons incident), assuming independent events. We write the chance or probability of such a jump per second for each particle as

$$an_i,$$

where n_i is the number of resonant photons incident per second and a is the constant of proportionality whose magnitude is determined by such factors as the frequency of the electromagnetic waves, the kind of particle, and the direction of polarization of the photons. The coefficient a has been and is the subject of a great deal of physical research and study.

Each of the N_1 particles has this same chance of being stimulated to absorb a resonant photon provided the net absorption remains small. So the number of photons absorbed out of the beam per second is

$$an_iN_1.$$

The loss of photons should be a way of counting the number of particles in the lower level.

What about the particles in the upper level? How do we count N_2? Those particles cannot absorb resonant photons—they have no way of storing the extra energy. However, each of the N_2 particles can drop down to the lower level and *emit* a photon into the beam. In fact, the presence of the n_i photons does stimulate this emission process in the same manner as the stimulated absorption. *Stimulated emission* occurs by pure chance, with the *same probability* of a per photon per particle per second. So the number of photons added to the beam by stimulated emission is an_iN_2, and we have a measure of the number in the upper level.

We will also find *in every situation* a few photons emitted spontaneously by particles in the upper level. This spontaneous process also occurs by pure chance, but depends only on the type of particle, the number capable of such emission (N_2 in our case) and the type of container for the beam. It does *not* depend on the presence of the beam. Therefore, we may write the number of photons spontaneously emitted into the beam as bN_2. These are familiar photons, since we see them *spontaneously emitted* from such places as fluorescent lamps and the surface of the sun.

Now our counting seems confused—by thermal noise, of course. The number of (identical) transmitted photons is

$$n_t = n_i - an_iN_1 + an_iN_2 + bN_2. \tag{4.18}$$

If possible, we like to simplify things by working at power levels well above spontaneous emission. Hence, we use large enough values of n_i to be able to neglect the last term bN_2, and we expect the transmission to be

$$n_t/n_i = 1 - a(N_1 - N_2), \tag{4.19}$$

giving us our particle count.

By measuring the transmission n_t/n_i, we get a number which is a useful measure of the excess of population N_1 over population N_2. In the normal temperature range (N_1 greater than N_2) we will find the number to be always less than one. In other words, we find *net absorption* from our beam.

But what about the value of a? The details of the particular mechanism by which our beam of electromagnetic energy stimulates resonance absorption and emission have many interesting features. For example, the polarization required for driving electric dipoles is a parallel electric field, but to apply synchronous torque to the magnetic moments of spins requires a perpendicular rotating magnetic field. The value of the probability a is dependent on the frequency of the incident photons, going to zero far off resonance. The effective value of a is necessarily a positive number very much less than one. Therefore, according to Eq. 4.19, every sample with N_1 greater than N_2 gives *net absorption*.

Now, let's look at such a measurement. For our sample of F-centers in KCl, we choose an applied field H from the resonance condition $f = \gamma H_0$, in order to have a convenient frequency. Putting the sample containing 1×10^{16} spins in a microwave cavity in boiling liquid helium, in a field near 3200 oersteds, we find a net absorption of the resonance radiation at $f = 9000$ megacycles per second, as shown in the photograph in Fig. 4.8. The horizontal scale shows a small varia-

Power Transmitted

1.0

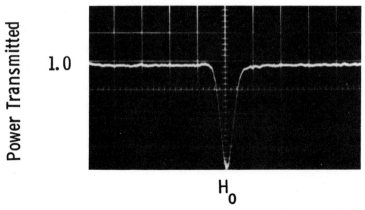

H_0

(*Westinghouse Research Laboratories.*)

Figure 4.8 Net resonance absorption. The oscilloscope photograph shows resonance absorption in a sample of 1×10^{16} F-center spins in a crystal of *KCl* at $T = 4.2°$K and $H_o = 3200$ oersteds. The absorption of the 9000 megacycle per second radiation indicates the spin temperature was also $+4.2°$K.

tion in the applied magnetic field (through the resonance condition at H_0). The vertical scale is effectively the transmission coefficient n_i/n_t, with net absorption being down from the horizontal line of transparency, $n_i/n_t = 1$. The net absorption seen in the photograph is just the amount expected from a 5 percent excess in the lower level from Eq. 4.19. Therefore, the spin temperature, calculated by Eq. 4.9, gives T_s equal to the lattice temperature at $4.2°$K. This equality was expected, because we waited a long time before taking the photograph, in order to obtain equilibrium between spin energy and lattice energy.

Looking again at Eq. 4.19, we can see one of the startling characteristics of negative temperatures. With a negative temperature describing the populations of the two spin levels, the excess is a deficit. With N_2 greater than N_1, n_t becomes larger than n_i and we get out more resonant photons than we put in. This is obviously *net emission*, resulting from an inverted distribution.

In seeking a method of obtaining an inverted distribution, we recall the threat of ever-present relaxation. This means that in any real situation there is some heat flow, and therefore the temperatures representing the separable energy forms will relax toward the blended or thermal temperatures; in some instances this relaxation may be gradual.

In our two-level system, relaxation may be considered qualitatively in the following sense. We recognize that the individual particles in level #2 are making jumps to level #1, and vice versa, but we know so little about the jumps that we say they occur by pure chance in some average time. We can write the average dwell time for a particle in level #2 before it makes a trip to level #1 as τ_{21} and similarly, for level #1, the time τ_{12}. Starting with populations other than the equilibrium ones, $N_1(\infty)$ and $N_2(\infty)$, the number added to level #2, dN_2, in the interval of time dt is

$$\frac{dN_2}{dt} = -\frac{N_2(t)}{\tau_{21}} + \frac{N_1(t)}{\tau_{12}}. \tag{4.20}$$

Now, we know from the equilibrium populations $N_1(\infty) = N_2(\infty)e^{S/kT}$ that $\tau_{12} = \tau_{21}e^{S/kT}$. Using the conservation of particles,

$$N = N_1(t) + N_2(t),$$

and a little algebra, we find the relaxation of N_2 proceeding as

$$\frac{dN_2(t)}{dt} = -\frac{N_2(t) - N_2(\infty)}{\tau}, \tag{4.21}$$

where
$$\tau = \tau_{21}/(1 + e^{-S/kT}). \tag{4.22}$$

We find that Eq. 4.21 says that the population $N_2(t)$ approaches its equilibrium value $N_2(\infty)$ with increasing time in an exponential fashion, since the instantaneous rate of change is proportional to the remaining deviation from its final value. In other words, in every period of time equal to the time constant τ, the deviation of N_2 from $N_2(\infty)$ is reduced by a factor of $1/e = 1/2.732 \ldots$ The time constant τ is called the *relaxation time;* it is, by Eq. 4.22, at large values of temperature T, closely one half the average dwell time. It is interesting to note that the exponential relaxation, described, for example, in the last equation, allows us to obtain conditions very close to equilibrium. We are generally quite content to wait long enough to have other sources of fluctuation or deviation be as large as the remaining relaxation, and then to accept that condition as "equilibrium."

For two levels all alone, and at a strictly conserved total number N, the largest initial deviation we can get is to interchange N_1 and N_2. This inversion of the populations is accomplished for magnetic spins by a process called *adiabatic fast passage*, in which we rely on their gyroscopic or precessional property, and sweep through the resonance condition with a very strong rotating field in a time short compared to the relaxation time τ. The word *adiabatic*, in this description, means that the passage is slow enough for the precession of each spin to follow the changing effective magnetic field, as the resonance condition is swept through. The only other way to obtain inversion of a spin with just two levels all alone is to apply synchronous torque just long enough to have each spin flip to the other level; this latter technique is called *180° pulse* and is generally useful only at low frequencies.

An example of inversion, or interchange, of populations in our KCl sample can be seen in Fig. 4.9. The photograph, taken a few minutes after inversion, shows the net increase in transmitted radiation, under the same inspecting sweep as for the equilibrium condition of Fig. 4.8. The increase, in Fig. 4.9, shows a negative temperature of about $-10°K$.

The negative temperature, pictured in Fig. 4.9, could be useful since it represents net stimulated emission. This increase in resonance radiation by the sample of F-center spins could be used to amplify incoming resonance radiation in properly engineered circumstances. Such an amplifier is called a *maser*. The name, derived from *M*icrowave *A*mplification using *S*timulated *E*mission of *R*adiation, was first applied to the ammonia beam oscillator by Drs. J. P. Gordon and

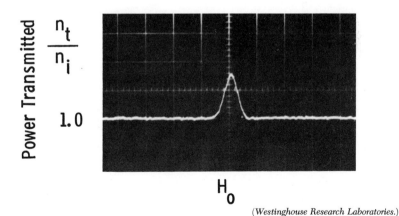

(*Westinghouse Research Laboratories.*)

Figure 4.9 Net resonance emission from two levels all alone. The oscilloscope photograph shows resonance emission one minute after inversion of the spin populations in the same sample of F-centers used for Fig. 4.8. The net emission indicates the spin temperature was $-10°K$.

H. J. Zeiger, and Professor C. H. Townes, in their original demonstration of net gain, in 1954. The principal advantage of the maser is that it is relatively noise-free. The low-noise characteristic of masers is expected, because all the active elements or parts are at low values of temperature. In our example (Fig. 4.9) the metal cavity containing the beam of resonance radiation was at $+4.2°K$, and the F-center spins at $-10°K$. Therefore, the expected noise would be somewhat larger than the normal thermal noise from a cavity at $+10°K$. The temperature of the crystal containing the F-centers was not important (except for longer relaxation) because the crystal does not contribute loss to the beam directly. Full utilization of such low-noise properties should remain an exciting engineering challenge for many years.

An oscillator is readily made from an amplifier with enough gain. Maser oscillators are in considerable demand, because their low-noise properties often show up as extreme frequency stability. A few applications will be mentioned later.

What do we expect the relaxation to do? It should have destroyed our negative temperature condition, of course. And it did. The inverted populations of F-center spins did relax from their almost fully inverted condition of Fig. 4.9 to their "equilibrium" condition of Fig. 4.8 with the passing of time. The series of photographs in Fig. 4.10 shows this relaxation, with the transmission measurement repeated at succeeding times. The recovery obeyed the relaxation Eq. 4.19 with a time constant of about thirty minutes. We see that F-center populations were observed to be described by negative temperatures for only a few minutes, following inversion at $4.2°K$ and 3000 oersteds. With two levels all alone, negative temperatures are available only for short times, followed inevitably by rather long periods of relaxation.

To demonstrate that such negative temperatures do give net amplification, a large sample of spins, with energy levels very similar to the energy levels of the F-centers, was cycled from equilibrium through inversion to equilibrium. The resonance condition was swept through repeatedly at successive delay times from zero (shortly after inversion) to 100 milliseconds (near to equilibrium). The effect on the incident radiation is shown in Fig. 4.11, where net gain occurs on each sweep up to 1.5 milliseconds. Net gain was thus available for a small fraction of the cycle.

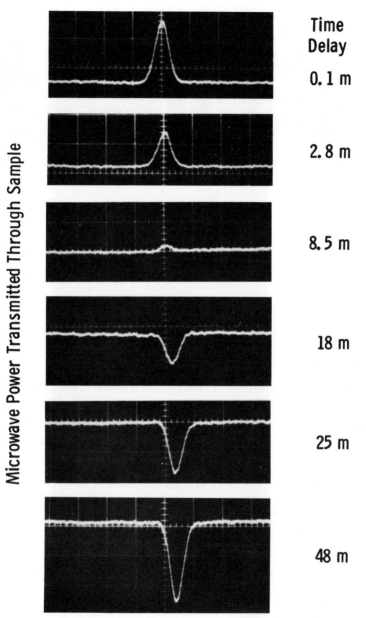

Time
Delay

0. 1 m

2. 8 m

8. 5 m

18 m

25 m

48 m

Microwave Power Transmitted Through Sample

(*Westinghouse Research Laboratories.*)

Figure 4.10 Relaxation in two levels all alone. The series of oscilloscope photographs, taken separately at successive time delays after inversion show relaxation of the F-centers from the negative temperature of Fig. 4.9 toward the equilibrium condition of Fig. 4.8. The numbers on the right side indicate the time delay for each in minutes.

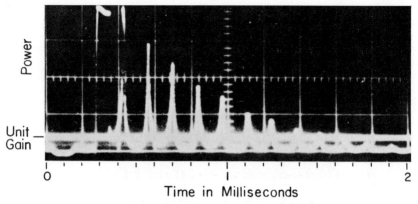

(*Westinghouse Research Laboratories.*)

Figure 4.11 Time dependence of gain for a pulsed two-level maser. Each sharp peak that reaches above the horizontal line of unit gain shows net gain from the maser as the magnetic field is swept through the resonance condition.

The pulsed inversion of another two-level system—proton spins— has been used to measure the earth's magnetic field to a very high precision. This device together with many ideas basic to the concept and use of negative temperatures is discussed beautifully by Professor A. Abragam in his book, *The Principles of Nuclear Magnetism*. Pulsed inversion is a significant research tool, although lacking in general practical significance. It is currently being used to increase our understanding of the detailed nature of such simple equilibrium configurations as F-centers in crystals, as well as the dynamic processes by which energy changes hands from spins to phonons.

For practical use of maser amplification or oscillation, we would like continuous negative temperatures. To maintain these, however, we must have either more than two levels or a constantly changing collection of particles (adding particles in level #2 and removing particles from level #1). The latter technique was used in the ammonia beam maser by sending the beam of "inverted" ammonia molecules continuously through the microwave cell; the active populations included only those molecules that were inside the cell at any instant.

TWO LEVELS ALWAYS UPSIDE DOWN

How can we get the populations of our sample of F-centers to stay continuously inverted? The problem of maintaining two levels continuously inverted is one of battling relaxation, without introducing noise. To accomplish this, can we use a third higher level? Inspection of the energy level diagram of Fig. 4.7 suggests one possibility. We can try to pump preferentially out of level #1 into level #3 and rely on random return to both levels #1 and #2, hoping to obtain N_1 greater than N_2. Actually, we have tried this in the laboratory, but only with unpolarized light; our best efforts to date are represented in Fig. 4.12.

In this photograph we see evidence for equality of N_1 and N_2, when the pump light is on. We were not losing any F-centers because the absorption returned to the value shown in Fig. 4.8, with a time constant of thirty minutes after the light was turned off. More research is needed on this possibility of continuous negative temperatures.

Now, looking around for other particles that might perform more suitably, we find many interesting and useful ones. One that is often used to very good practical advantage is the assembly of a nucleus of mass 52 and twenty-one electrons. Such an assembly is called the *chromium +3 ion*. For our present discussion, it will serve as one particle. The energy level populations of collections of Cr(+3) ions hold several possibilities for negative temperatures.

The energy forms of interest for a Cr(+3) ion, located substitutionally in an ionic dielectric crystal, are the spin energy in an external

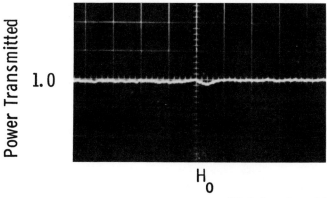

(*Westinghouse Research Laboratories.*)

Figure 4.12 Optical pumping of F-centers. The oscilloscope photograph shows the *KCl* crystal to be transparent, even at the resonance condition. The transparency of the F-center sample of Fig. 4.8 was effected at 2.1°K by the absorption of 10^{13} photons per second between the lower pair of levels and level 3 of Fig. 4.7.

magnetic field, and the electrostatic energy stored by the Cr(+3) ion in the field of its diamagnetic neighboring ions. A few of the energy levels of the latter form are indicated in Fig. 4.13 for two host crystals, MgO and Al_2O_3. The distribution without pumping is all the particles in #1. For interaction with resonance radiation, the selection rules in both crystals are such that external radiation is strongly absorbed between #1 and #3, and weakly absorbed between #1 and #2. However, in level #3 the internal electric energy of the particles is not isolated from the kinetic energy of the lattice—far from it. Every particle, excited from level #1 to level #3, makes a quick trip immediately to level #2, with the help of the lattice (as an energy sink). The particle in level #2 waits for either spontaneous emission

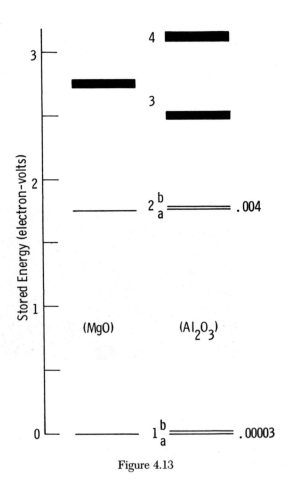

Figure 4.13

or for forced emission by resonance radiation of energy $E_2 - E_1$ (red photons) or for some other means of getting rid of its stored energy, such as making a large number of lattice vibrations. The spontaneous emission for $Cr(+3)$ is relatively slow; the natural lifetime in level #2 has been observed to be a few milliseconds for both Al_2O_3 and MgO. This is the coefficient b in Eq. 4.18. Therefore, if every particle removed from #1 to #3 quickly ends up in #2, and if we can put in photons of energy $E_3 - E_1$ (green light) fast enough, we should get more particles in #2 than in #1. If we could keep on pumping fast enough, we would be able to maintain N_2 greater than N_1.

Is this describable by a temperature? Our sample now consists of N identical chromium $+3$ ions, substituted for a few of the aluminum ions in a crystal of Al_2O_3, in other words, a ruby. The time spent in level #3 (Fig. 4.13) is so small (of the order of a micromicrosecond) that the populations can be written: $N = N_1 + N_2$ and $N_3 = 0$. Then all the preceding analysis for two levels applies, and the inverted condition (N_2 greater than N_1) represents a negative temperature, which should be very useful.

The red fluorescence (spontaneous emission #2 to #1) from ruby has been known for a long time; this occurs for any N_2 greater than zero. Recently, sufficient pump power has been poured into ruby to get N_2 greater than N_1. The result is the availability of net stimulated emission of the red resonance light, in a device called a *laser*, or *optical maser*. By silvering over most of the two ends of a ruby rod, the feedback is raised to the point of oscillation and a very bright, nearly monochromatic beam of light is obtained. The focusing properties of such light are quite remarkable. Fig. 4.14 shows the red spot from such a laser rod, without a lens, at a distance of about one yard. The intensity of a ruby laser has been raised to the point where such a beam may blind a person a mile away.

There are still considerable difficulties with obtaining laser performance at arbitrary light frequencies; the opportunities and the challenges are many. There may even be conditions in which a laser can have internal equilibrium in addition to a negative temperature, for its two populated energy levels.

Another range of significance is apparent upon closer inspection of the energy levels of $Cr(+3)$. In a magnetic field of about 3000 oersteds, we find the energy levels to be as shown in Fig. 4.15 for ruby,

(Courtesy of R. D. Haun, T. A. Osial, and R. Williams
of the Westinghouse Research Laboratories.)

Figure 4.14 Light from a ruby laser. The bright spot shows the red light beam intercepted by a photographic plate located at a distance of 3 feet from the ruby rod (which measured $\frac{1}{4}$ inch in diameter and 2 inches long). The rings around the central spot show the cones of light which spread outside of the central beam. The chromium ($+3$) ions in the Al_2O_3 were pumped into level 2a of Fig. 4.13 via either level 3 or level 4. This photograph is actual size, taken without lenses.

the previous energy level labeled 1a is a pair, 1b is a pair, and likewise with 2a and 2b; for MgO, level $\#1$ splits up into four equally spaced levels, and likewise for $\#2$. The magnetic splittings are in the microwave range.

A very clever pumping scheme for continuous inversion was recently suggested by Professor N. Bloembergen of Harvard University. Expanding the scale of energy, we can picture the population distributions among the levels of the ground state, as in Fig. 4.16, with equilibrium populations for $4.2°K$ and 3000 oersteds shown on the left; there are many possible pump schemes as shown on the right. The pumping effect is to equalize at least one pair of populations, a and c, for example. Then, by natural relaxation, the population of b is either greater than, equal to, or less than the populations of a and c. There is continuous inversion available in two of these cases. Many useful and extremely sensitive microwave amplifiers, based on this type of pumping scheme, have been constructed and are now being used.

In what sense is the inversion available in one of Bloembergen's schemes described by a negative temperature? Clearly there is no one temperature that applies to all four levels. But the populations of the four levels are each remaining constant in time, and therefore if the sample is restricted to being just those spins in the two levels with inverted populations, such as a and b as in Fig. 4.16, it is possible to specify a negative spin temperature, as in Eq. 4.15. The analy-

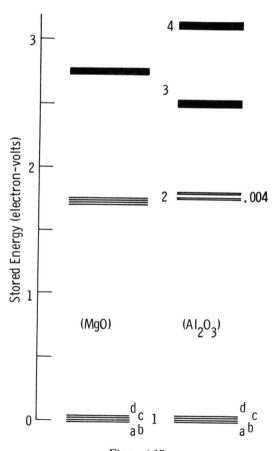

Figure 4.15

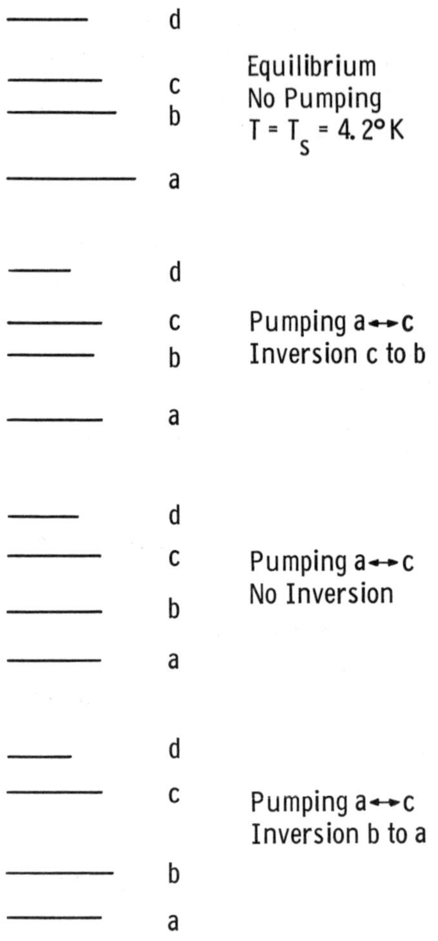

Figure 4.16 Population distributions of $Cr\ (+3)$ ions in Al_2O_3 in a magnetic field.

sis leading to Eq. 4.19 applies with $N' = N_1 + N_2$, and the populations of a and b can vary over the negative temperature range, depending on the effectiveness of the pumping.

FOUR LEVELS INVERTED

A close inspection of the lowest four energy levels of the chromium $+3$ ion in the cubic site in a crystal of MgO shows them to be equally spaced, with the spacing proportional to the applied magnetic field, as expressed by Eq. 4.5. The Zeeman energy separation is 9000 mega-

cycles per second in a field of 3200 oersteds. The populations of
$Cr+3$ ions in equilibrium with a lattice temperature of 4.2°K and
H = 3200 oersteds are shown by the lengths of the horizontal bars on
Fig. 4.17; this distribution gives rise to net absorption of the resonance
radiation of 9000 megacycles per second. A tracing of a photograph
of such resonance absorption is shown in Fig. 4.17a.

No continuous inversion via a pumping scheme similar to Bloembergen's seems feasible. Let's look at pulsed inversion. Inversion by
fast passage works well; in fact, inversion of all four populations is
accomplished at one sweep. Figure 4.17b shows a tracing of a photograph taken following adiabatic fast passage; it corresponds to the
inverted distribution of Fig. 4.17b and shows *net emission* for the
resonance condition.

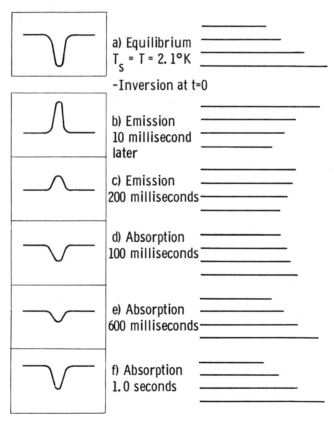

Figure 4.17 Population distributions and resonance transmission of chromium (+3)
ions at 2.1°K in *MgO*.

Relaxation, of course, takes place. The effect of relaxation on the transmission of the microwaves by the crystal can be seen in the series of tracings in Fig. 4.17. For $Cr(+3)$ spins in MgO, the relaxation has a single time constant, τ, as expected with the three transitions coincident. For $4.2°K$, we observe τ to be $\frac{1}{4}$ second, a value fortuitously close to that calculated on the very simple model of an MgO crystal being made up of point charges of $+2$ vibrating in place of the Mg ions, and -2 in place of the oxygen ions.

A continuous pumping scheme might be possible for chromium in MgO if we were to use "red" photons (of energy $E_2 - E_1$ in Fig. 4.13) to pump preferentially out of the lower spin levels. Referring to Figs. 4.13 and 4.15, we would arrange things so that $Cr(+3)$ ions would be pumped much faster from the lower levels ($\#$1a and $\#$1b) than from the upper ones ($\#$1c and $\#$1d). By this *optical pumping* we would hope to maintain the four spin levels continuously inverted; the experiment has not been tried yet for lack of a light source of sufficient intensity.

APPLICATIONS OF NEGATIVE TEMPERATURES

The scope of applications of negative and infinite temperatures is so wide as to be a severe test of one's imagination. We will mention a few of the devices that have already been demonstrated in order to gain a more lasting impression of the challenges open to the inquiring and to the ingenious.

Starting with the low frequency range, where low noise amplification is available without the negative temperatures of masers, several masers have been built which measure small changes in the earth's magnetic field. Such sensitive magnetometers are and will be a versatile means for surveying the character of the crust of the earth, and a source of some satisfaction in our nation's defense ability. In fact, one commercial unit employing a spin temperature which has either a negative value or a value about one-thousandth that of the surroundings is being used in surveying snow avalanches for buried people and paraphernalia.

In the microwave range, maser preamplifiers are and will be used with radio telescopes to map the skies. Expectations are that such telescopes will have a much longer range than the 200-inch optical tele-

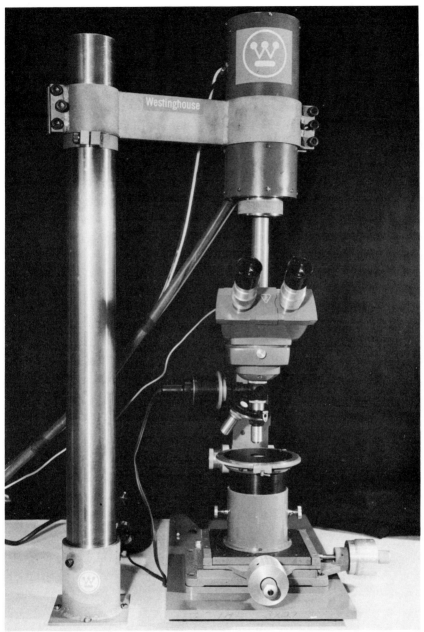

(Westinghouse Research Laboratories.)

A ruby laser being used as a light source for a binocular microscope. The pulsed red light from the laser is sufficiently intense and can be focused to a sufficiently small spot to permit drastic local heating to be observed on a microscopic scale. Applications include examinations of biological specimens.

scope on Mount Palomar, due to the low-noise amplification available in the masers. Maser preamplifiers for radar will become more useful as the present art is slowly converted to an engineering technology. Currently, a maser oscillator using the natural resonance frequency of cesium atoms is the world's standard clock. An even better time standard is expected soon in the form of a hydrogen bottle maser. Masers in the millimeter and far infrared region will probably open up this heretofore restricted region to research in spectroscopy and eventually to practical devices.

In the infrared and the visible range, lasers will be used for everything from writing one's initials on the back of a bacterium to sending a long message across the open space of the sky. The beautiful experiments possible with a coherence length of miles simply stagger one's normally wild imagination.

5

Fermi, Dirac, Bose, and Einstein

IN CHAPTER THREE, we determined in a simple way the manner in which particles are distributed among their energy levels. To do this, we had to count the number of ways a given distribution could arise, and it was assumed that all the particles were distinguishable—that is, they could be told apart. Thus, we assumed that the distribution in Fig. 3.5a would occur in three ways; we could tell if particle A, B, or C was in the top level. In principle at least, this is possible for the atoms in a solid. Each atom has its equilibrium position and is known by its particular position. However, in the case of a gas this is no longer true. The gas molecule moves chaotically through the enclosure, and therefore there is nothing that distinguishes one atom of the gas from another. We might wonder if the state of Fig. 3.5a should be counted as occurring in three ways, or in one way. Clearly, if we assume that we should count it as three ways, the distribution we calculate for a gas would differ from that of a solid. However, if we count the state of Fig. 3.5a only once, we see that quite a difference in distribution will arise. Theory alone cannot tell us what to do. This is another case where we must reveal our ignorance and simply make an assumption that agrees with experiment.

In the following, we will assume that the state of Fig. 3.5a can arise in only *one way* in a gas. We will find that this assumption is in accord with experiment. In scientific language, we refer to the particles in solids as distinguishable (by their positions), and as indistinguishable in a gas. It will be seen that this leads to a very fundamental difference in the distribution of particles among their energy levels.

There is one further difference between a gas and a solid. In treating the solid, it was fundamental that the atoms could only take on certain energy values. The same situation holds in the gas. However, quantum theory tells us that the spacing of the energy levels is inversely proportional to the volume of the container. In a solid, an atom is confined to a "container" approximately 10^{-8} cm on a side; that is, each atom is confined by its nearest neighbors in the solid. However, in a gas, each atom normally has a volume of 1 cm^3 or more in which to move around. Thus, the energy level spacing in a gas is some 10^{24} times less than in a solid. This means that the energy levels can be treated almost as if they were continuous.

DISTRIBUTION FOR INDISTINGUISHABLE PARTICLES (FERMI-DIRAC TYPE)

Using this information, we may now calculate what distributions have the maximum value of ω, for a system of N particles having a total energy E. Since the levels are so closely spaced as to be almost continuous, we will group the levels into batches such that all the levels in a given batch have essentially the same energy, as shown in Fig. 5.1. We will label the batches 0, 1, 2, 3, and so on, in order of increasing energy. We will assume that the number of particles in each batch is n_0, n_1, n_2, n_3, and so forth, and that the first batch contains N_0 levels, and so on. We now need to calculate the number of

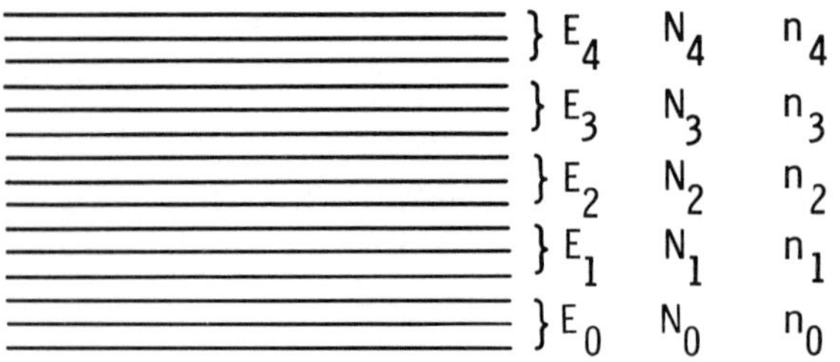

Figure 5.1

ways in which we can distribute n_1 particles on N_1 levels, n_2 particles on N_2 levels, and so on. Clearly, the possible arrangements of n_1 particles on N_1 levels are independent of the possible arrangements of n_2 particles on N_2 levels. Thus the total number of arrangements, ω, of the two groups of particles is simply equal to the product of the number of arrangements of the first batch with that of the second. It follows, then, that the total ω for the whole system is the product of the arrangements of each batch of levels.

Before making this calculation, it is necessary to introduce one additional complication. So far we have considered that each energy level may contain an arbitrary number of particles. This is not always true. For certain particles, such as electrons and protons, experiment has made it necessary to assume that only one particle may be found in any given level. (Actually, if the *spin* of the particles is considered, there may be two particles per level.) For other particles, there is no limitation on the number of particles per level. Whether the particle is of the first type or the second type can only be determined by experiment. We will treat just the first type here.

Let's now calculate the ω_i (that is, the number of possible ways of placing n_i particles on N_i levels, assuming a maximum of one particle per level) for the ith batch of levels. We need to know the number of ways in which n_i particles can be distributed over N_i levels with no more than one particle per level. This is the same as asking, "In how many ways can we distribute n_i particles and $N_i - n_i$ holes ("absence" of particles) among N_i levels?" From previous experience with this type of problem, we can see that

$$\omega_i = \frac{N_i!}{n_i! \, (N_i - n_i)!}. \tag{5.1}$$

Then the ω for the whole group of levels would be simply the product of all the ω_i's. In what follows, we will examine a set of three consecutive batches of levels. Thus,

$$\omega = \frac{N_1!}{n_1! \, (N_1 - n_1)!} \times \frac{N_2!}{n_2! \, (N_2 - n_2)!} \times \frac{N_3!}{n_3! \, (N_3 - n_3)!}. \tag{5.2}$$

Now we may follow the same procedure as before. We want to find those values of the n_i's which make ω a maximum. We may do this by again examining our set of three consecutive batches of levels. As before, we remove two particles from the middle batch, placing one particle in the lower batch and one particle in the upper batch. Since we have assumed that our batches are equally spaced, on an energy scale, this process does not change the energy of the system. Furthermore, the number of particles clearly stays constant. After the transferal has taken place, ω may be written

$$\omega_{final} = \frac{N_1!}{(n_1 + 1)! \, (N_1 - n_1 - 1)!} \times \frac{N_2!}{(n_2 - 2)! \, (N_2 - n_2 + 2)!}$$
$$\times \frac{N_3!}{(n_3 + 1)! \, (N_3 - n_3 - 1)!} . \qquad (5.3)$$

Taking Eq. 5.2 as $\omega_{initial}$, we may easily show by methods previously introduced that

$$\frac{\omega_{final}}{\omega_{initial}} = \frac{N_1 - n_1}{n_1} \left[\frac{n_2}{(N_2 - n_2)} \right]^2 \frac{N_3 - n_3}{n_3} . \qquad (5.4)$$

Now if we use the symbol

$$P_i = \frac{N_i - n_i}{n_i} , \qquad (5.5)$$

Eq. 5.4 may be rewritten

$$\frac{\omega_{final}}{\omega_{initial}} = \frac{P_1 P_3}{P_2{}^2} . \qquad (5.6)$$

As in previous cases, we know that ω is a maximum when the right side of Eq. 5.6 is equal to unity. Thus we see that in this case, the P's follow the same relationship as the n's for the classical case. To find the distribution having maximum ω, we must solve Eq. 5.6. In analogy with Eq. 3.10 and 3.13 we may write

$$P_i = A' e^{\mu E_i} = \frac{N_i - n_i}{n_i} , \qquad (5.7)$$

or

$$\frac{n_i}{N_i} = \frac{1}{A' e^{\mu E_i} + 1} . \qquad (5.8)$$

We see that there are again two arbitrary parameters A' and μ. These parameters may be eliminated as before by using the conditions that

$$n_1 + n_2 + n_3 = n, \tag{5.9}$$

and

$$E_1 n_1 + E_2 n_2 + E_3 n_3 = E. \tag{5.10}$$

At this point, we could again show that the parameter μ of Eq. 5.7 is related to the temperature. If we use the P's of Eq. 5.5 instead of the n's of Eq. 3.22, the argument carries through in the same manner as when the particles are distinguishable. It can be shown that μ should be set equal to $1/kT$.

It is now worthwhile to examine Eq. 5.8 carefully. The quantity n_i/N_i represents the average occupancy of the ith batch of levels. Since each of these levels has essentially the same energy, we may as well take this quantity to be the average occupancy, or the average number of particles, in a level of energy E_i. Thus if we now use n_i to designate the average number of particles in a level of energy E_i, we may write

$$n_i = \frac{1}{A' e^{\mu E_i} + 1}. \tag{5.11}$$

Or again, using $\mu = \dfrac{1}{kT}$,

$$n_i = \frac{1}{A' e^{E_i/kT} + 1}. \tag{5.12}$$

This distribution is called the Fermi-Dirac distribution and should be compared with the result of Chapter Three derived for distinguishable particles. The classical distribution according to Eq. 3.13 was

$$n_i = A e^{-E_i/kT}. \tag{5.13}$$

If we now rewrite Eq. 5.13 in the form

$$n_i = \frac{1}{A e^{E_i/kT}},$$

we see that the sole difference between the distribution for distinguishable particles and that for indistinguishable particles is the presence of a unity in the denominator. Let's now try to understand the consequences of this unity. The first and obvious consequence is that it enforces our requirement that there be only one particle per level, for no matter what the value of $A' e^{E_i/kT}$ may be, n_i must be equal to or less than one. Now examine the distribution of Eq. 5.12 at a given temperature. Remember A' depends only on temperature and the total number of particles and was introduced so that the conditions of Eqs. 5.9 and 5.10 could be satisfied. Therefore, for our present discussion, at a fixed temperature and a fixed number of particles, A' may be treated as constant. Now, clearly, no matter how small A' may be, there must be some energy E_i at which $A'e^{E_i/kT}$ is much greater than the unity. When this is so, we may neglect the unity in the denominator of Eq. 5.12 and write

$$n_i = \frac{1}{A'e^{E_i/kT}}. \tag{5.14}$$

We see that the result is identical to that of Eq. 5.13 for distinguishable particles. Hence, we have our first observation. *Beyond a certain energy level, the distribution will be the same as in the classical case.* It follows that in the classical region (for a gas), the number of particles per energy level is much less than 1. (Remember each level can hold a maximum of 1 particle in the case of the Fermi-Dirac distribution.)

Having looked at the very high energy region, let's look again, beginning at zero on the energy scale. We will choose some arbitrary value for the constant A'. Let's say 10^{-6}. (Remember A' reflects only the total number of particles and the number of energy levels in the system.) At $E_i = 0$, we have

$$n_i = \frac{1}{10^{-6} + 1}.$$

Thus the level at $E = 0$ is almost certainly occupied. Even at the energy level where $E_i/kt \simeq 10$, we see from Eq. 5.12 that the chance of occupancy is still about 98 percent. If we plot a graph of n_i versus E_i/kT, using Eq. 5.12, as shown in Fig. 5.2, we see that n_i drops rapidly in the vicinity of $A'e^{E_i/kT} = 1$. If we continue to talk of higher and higher energies, we know we will reach the point noted above; that is, the classical region. This occurs when $A'e^{E_i/kT}$ becomes much greater than unity. Thus we see that essentially all levels are occupied up to energies where $A'e^{E_i/kT} \gtrsim 1$. This is an important result.

Now, we recall that in the example just discussed, we set $A' = 10^{-6}$. This was done completely arbitrarily. We have not, so far, placed any restriction on the possible values of A'. From the above discussion, we easily see that were A' smaller, the levels would be significantly occupied to a higher energy. In fact, the smaller A', the higher in energy we must go before we are likely to find an empty level. Now let's see what happens when A' gets larger. We saw that when $A'e^{E_i/kT}$ becomes large compared to unity, we had the classical distribution law. Obviously, as A' gets larger the classical distribution will obtain over more and more of the energy scale. In fact, if A' is of the order of 10, we see that the classical region extends essentially down to $E_i = 0$. Is this possible? To answer, let's examine more carefully what determines A'. If we assume that the classical region extends over the whole energy scale, then we know from Eq. 5.14 that

$$n_i = \frac{1}{A'e^{E_i/kT}} = A'^{-1}e^{-E_i/kT}. \tag{5.15}$$

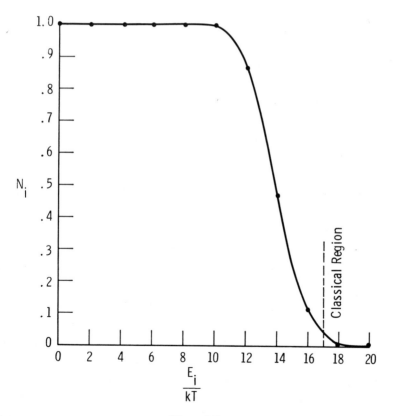

Figure 5.2

To determine A', we use the fact that there are n particles in the system. Thus,

$$n = \sum_{i=0}^{\infty} n_i = \sum_{i=0}^{\infty} A'^{-1} e^{-E_i/kT} = A'^{-1} \sum_{i=0}^{\infty} e^{-E_i/kT} \qquad (5.16)$$

The A'^{-1} can be removed from under the summation sign as it is independent of i. Thus

$$A' = \frac{1}{n} \sum_{i=0}^{\infty} e^{-E_i/kT} = \frac{1}{n} \{ e^{-E_0/kT} + e^{-E_1/kT} + \cdots \}. \qquad (5.17)$$

We see from Eq. 5.17 that each energy level having an energy significantly less than kT will contribute of the order of $1/n$ to the value of A'. Those levels significantly above kT will contribute essentially zero. Therefore, to get a large value of A', it is necessary to have something like $10n$ energy levels with energy much less than kT. This will give A' of the order of 10. We see that as we go to lower and lower temperatures, this requirement gets more difficult to fulfill. For example, at $1000°K$, we need $10n$ levels within an energy $1000\ k$, whereas at $1°K$, we need 10 levels within $1\ k$. (Remember, k is the Boltzmann constant.) Using as our criterion for the classical region the presence of $10n$ levels within kT, it is clear that as we lower the temperature we will reach a point where our criterion is no longer satisfied. Below this temperature, we must use the more complex Fermi-Dirac law of Eq. 5.12.

The one remaining point is to ask, "What determines the spacing between energy levels?" As previously mentioned, this question can only be resolved by the use of *quantum theory;* however, we will quote the result here. Under the present conditions, the spacing depends upon two parameters. First, the energy level spacing is inversely proportional to the volume. Thus, in a gas the spacing will be less than in a liquid, which in turn is less than in a solid. We have already seen that the spacing in a gas and in a solid differs by a factor of approximately 10^{24}. Second, the energy level spacing depends inversely on the mass of the particle. Therefore, we will expect hydrogen gas to have the largest spacing among the common gases.

We conclude then that A' should be large for gases; the heavier the gas, the larger A'. It turns out that for almost all gases, A' is large enough that the classical distribution applies down to the lowest temperature yet achieved. Only in the lightest gases might we expect to find departures from the classical law.

THE BOSE-EINSTEIN DISTRIBUTION

So far all the discussions of this section have been based on the fact that we have limited the number of particles per energy level to one. When we remove this restriction and allow any number of particles per level (but still counting each distribution only once) we arrive at what is called the Bose-Einstein distribution. This distribution can be derived in a manner analogous to the Fermi-Dirac case. We will not do this here but simply state the result. The number of particles in the ith level is found to be

$$n_i = \frac{1}{A'' e^{E_i/kT} - 1}. \tag{5.18}$$

It is interesting to observe the minus sign here, replacing the plus sign of the Fermi-Dirac case. Whereas the plus sign tended to decrease the population of a given energy level, the minus sign clearly tends to increase it. We could now carry out an analysis similar to that for the Fermi-Dirac distribution. However, since the line of reasoning is so similar, we will not do it here. Suffice it to say that (1) beyond a certain energy level, the classical distribution will hold, (2) for almost all gases, the classical region extends down to zero energy at the lowest temperatures yet achieved.

There is one special point, however, to the Bose-Einstein distribution. Let's examine the denominator of Eq. 5.18 more carefully. It is clear that A'' must always be equal to or greater than unity. For if A'' were less than unity, we would have the ridiculous result that a negative number of particles were in the zero energy level. However, when A'' is essentially unity, we see that, because of the minus one, an anomalously large number of particles are in the states near the zero of energy. We must now ask ourselves under what conditions A'' approaches unity. In the case of the Fermi-Dirac distribution, we saw that A' varied inversely with the number of particles and directly with the number of energy levels located within approximately kT of the zero state. By identical arguments, it can be seen that A'' varies in the same manner. Hence, it is conceivable that A'' could approach unity at some temperature above $0°K$.

Let's follow the population of the lowest energy level as the temperature is decreased. At room temperature, we know that A'' is much greater than unity (the classical distribution holds). Thus the average population of the zero level is much less than unity. As we get to very low temperatures, the population in the lowest level can become exceedingly large if A'' is approaching unity. Superficially, it might appear that this explosion of the population of the lowest level would be gradual; however, an exact analysis shows that this effect actually occurs rather precipitously. This phenomenon is called the *Einstein condensation*. It remains to ask where we might expect to find this phenomenon. As we have already seen that A'' is essentially inversely proportional to the energy level spacing which, in turn, is proportional to the mass of the particle, we see that this condensation could only be expected in the very light gases such as hydrogen or helium. In the following chapter we will discuss the observation of this phenomenon in helium.

PART 3

Up and Down

6

Toward Absolute Zero

MATTER BEHAVES in all sorts of fascinating ways when the temperature is lowered from the range of our everyday experience to one-millionth of a degree absolute—the lowest available to man at present.

For the past fifty years a whole new branch of physics has been devoted to a study of the properties of matter in the low temperature range. Until recently, low temperature physics was very much an academic pursuit, having little or no practical application. During the past ten years, however, this situation has changed drastically; today *cryogenics*, as it is sometimes called, is becoming more and more an essential part of our lives. Giant rockets consume vast quantities of liquefied oxygen, *boiling* at $-423°$F. The steel industry, too, now uses large amounts of liquid oxygen, often made on the site. Radio telescopes that receive incredibly faint signals from stars in the outermost regions of outer space now use masers operating in liquid helium at 4°K to improve their sensitivity. Tiny superconducting magnets, also operating in liquid helium, produce magnetic fields of the order of 50 kilogauss with virtually no power expenditure. These are but a few of the fast-multiplying uses of cryogenics.

In this chapter, we are going to discuss not only the ways of pro-

TABLE 6.A

Gas	B.P. (°K)	Gas	B.P. (°K)
Freon$_{22}$	232.5	Nitrogen	77.3
Carbon dioxide	194.6	Neon	27.2
Ethylene	169.3	Hydrogen	20.4
Methane	111.7	He^4	4.2
Oxygen	90.1	He^3	3.2

ducing low temperatures, but some of the many interesting phenomena that occur in this region. Many of the devices we have mentioned are based on these phenomena.

In general, there are two ways of producing low temperatures; these involve the use of either liquefied gases or demagnetization techniques. By far the most common method of the two utilizes liquefied gases. The boiling points of some of these gases are shown in Table 6.A, extending fairly uniformly down to 3.2°K, the normal boiling point of He^3. For each gas, it is possible to obtain temperatures below the normal boiling point by "pumping on them." This pumping process affects liquefied gases in much the same way that high altitudes affect water, which in mountainous regions will boil at much lower temperature than at sea level. Liquid oxygen, for example, normally boils at 90.1°K, but by pumping on it, the boiling temperature can be reduced to 54.4°K. When pumping on liquid He^3, it is necessary to take suitable precautions, which will be described later, but it is possible with this technique to obtain temperatures as low as 0.3°K. Using liquefied gases in this way, we can effectively cover the range of temperatures from 0.3°K to 300°K.

The most familiar use of liquefied gas to obtain low temperatures, of course, is the ordinary household refrigerator or freezer. The principle of operation is shown schematically in Fig. 6.1.

Essentially, we have a closed system containing a gas under pressure. Usually one of the freons (CCl_2F_2) is used, for reasons of safety. As the freon is compressed, it becomes hot because of the work done on it, in much the same way the air from a bicycle pump becomes heated when we inflate a tire. A heat exchanger cools the hot, compressed gas, which then passes to a throttling valve. As it goes through this valve, the freon expands and, in expanding, work is done against the attractive molecular forces existing in the gas. Since the gas is thermally isolated during the throttling process, this work can only be done at the expense of the freon's internal energy, which means that the gas cools; in fact, it liquefies. The liquid freon travels to the cold chamber of the refrigerator, where it evaporates. The gas now returns to the compressor, and the cycle is repeated.

Many gas liquefiers operate in a similar manner, the principal difference being that the cycle is not closed and the liquefied gas is siphoned off for external use. The phenomenon of the gas being cooled by doing *internal work* is known as the *Joule-Thompson effect*. Actually, this effect can produce either a rise or a fall in temperature, depending on the relative magnitude of the repulsive and attractive forces between the gas molecules. At sufficiently high temperatures, the repulsive forces dominate, and the gas *heats* on expansion. This effect diminishes as the temperature decreases, until the *inversion* temperature is reached, below which the gas *cools* on expansion. For gases such as freon, nitrogen, and oxygen, the inversion point is above room temperature and hence there is no need for precooling. In the case of hydrogen and helium, however, the inversion point is well below room temperature, and precooling is necessary before we can liquefy these gases by this method.

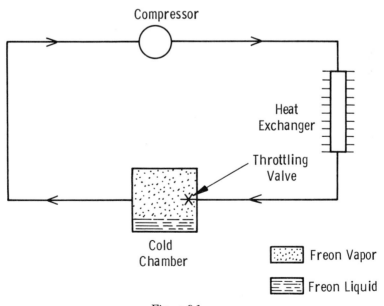

Figure 6.1

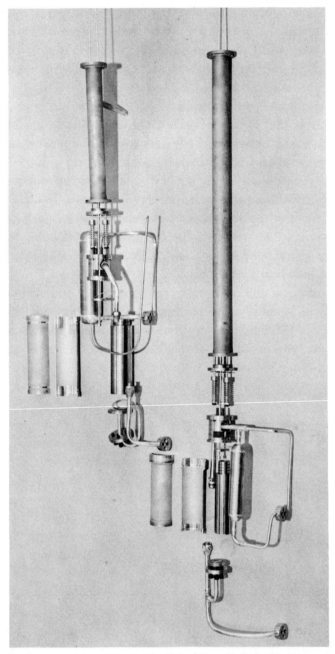

(Courtesy of Arthur D. Little, Inc., Cambridge, Massachusetts.)

Partially exploded views of two expansion engines for a Collins-type helium liquefier.

So far, we have considered only liquefiers that operate by doing internal work against the attractive forces existing within the gas itself. It is possible, however, to cool a gas by *adiabatic expansion,* accompanied by the performance of *external* work. In this case, no heat from the external surroundings can enter the gas, so that the external work can only be performed at the expense of the internal energy of the gas; the gas cools. Not only is this process more efficient, but there is the added advantage that a cooling *always* results, no matter what the initial temperature. The principal difficulty with the method of external work is that it necessitates the use of some sort of expansion system, similar to the piston and cylinder of an automobile engine. Just as the latter requires lubrication, so also does the expansion engine of the liquefier. Because the latter operates at low temperatures, however, we cannot use the usual lubricating oils. An ingenious solution to this problem is found in the Collins helium liquefier. This machine uses two expansion engines to cool the gaseous helium from liquid nitrogen temperature (77°K) to below its inversion temperature (15°K). Here the piston of each expansion engine has a large number of circumferential grooves along its length. Enough gas is trapped between these grooves and the wall of the cylinder to form a cushion, which effectively allows the piston to move in the cylinder without appreciable friction. The photograph shows partially exploded views of two of these expansion engines of a Collins-type liquefier. This kind of engine, which is used to liquefy helium in many scientific laboratories, is of interest since it uses the methods of both internal and external work to produce the liquefied gas. A diagrammatic sketch of the mode of operation of a Collins machine is shown in Fig. 6.2.

After compression to about 200 atmospheres, the gas passes to a heat exchanger, where it is cooled to a temperature of 77°K by an external supply of liquid nitrogen. Although this cooling is not absolutely necessary, it materially increases the efficiency and speed of liquefication. From the heat exchanger, the gas passes through the two expansion engines, where it undergoes further cooling to below its inversion temperature. During this process, the gas does external work against a braking device. After this, the gas is allowed to expand through a throttling valve, where it liquefies in the manner described previously.

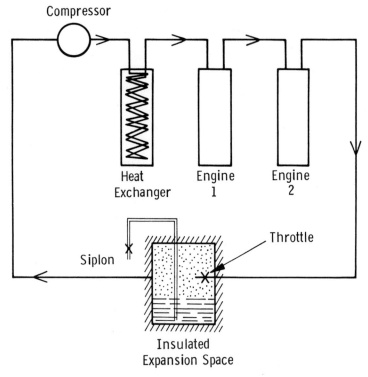

Figure 6.2

With proper adjustment, such a machine can produce about eight liters of liquid helium per hour. Such a liquefier is shown in the accompanying photograph, with the liquid being transferred into a glass storage vessel.

In storing liquid gases, the same principles are employed as those used to keep drinks cool for a picnic. To insulate the drinks from the surrounding air, it is necessary either to employ some material that is a poor conductor of heat, or else to use a vacuum flask, which is more effective. The construction of such a flask is shown diagrammatically in Fig. 6.3.

Basically, the device consists of a double-walled container, usually of silvered glass, with the space between the walls evacuated. After we have prepared the cool drink, we pour it into the container and cork it securely. Now, the only way in which the drink can warm up is by an influx of heat, by either radiation, convection, or conduction. Radiative heat transfer is reduced to a minimum by the silvering on the glass, since silver is a good reflector and prevents radiation from being transmitted through the glass. Because of the vacuum space, there is very little heat conduction between the walls, while the cork, being a poor conductor, prevents heat transfer across the mouth of the flask. The cork also prevents convection heat flow from the outside, so that the flask very effectively isolates its contents, thereby keeping them cool.

Precisely the same kind of vessels, called *Dewars* for their inventor, James Dewar, are used in a laboratory to store many liquefied gases, such as nitrogen, oxygen, and others. Naturally, Dewars made of glass are unsuitable for storing large quantities of liquefied gas, because they are not very strong mechanically. For this purpose, we use metal Dewars, whose walls are two concentric spheres made of polished copper to reduce losses by radiation. Each sphere is connected to a

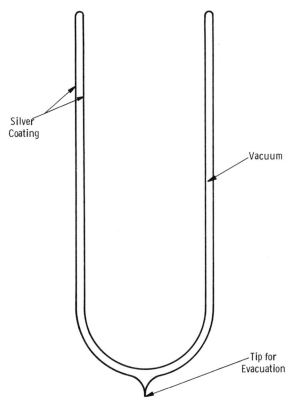

Figure 6.3

stainless steel neck, which is made long and narrow to minimize conduction from the surroundings. In the case of liquid hydrogen and helium, both of which have low latent heat of vaporization per unit volume, a simple storage vessel, such as that described, is not sufficient to prevent a large influx of heat from the surroundings. To reduce the rate of evaporation to any acceptable value, it is necessary in such cases to use a liquid nitrogen bath as a heat shield. Liquid nitrogen absorbs all the room temperature radiation from the exterior, and the only radiation reaching the inner liquid comes from material at the temperature of the nitrogen itself, 77°K. Now, from Stefan's law, we

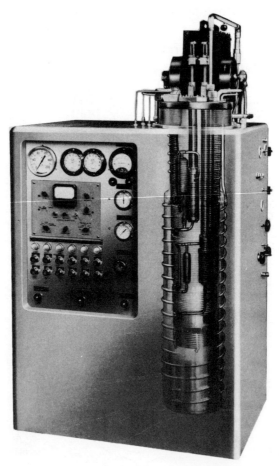

(Courtesy of Arthur D. Little, Inc., Cambridge, Massachusetts.)

Cutaway view of a Collins liquefier.

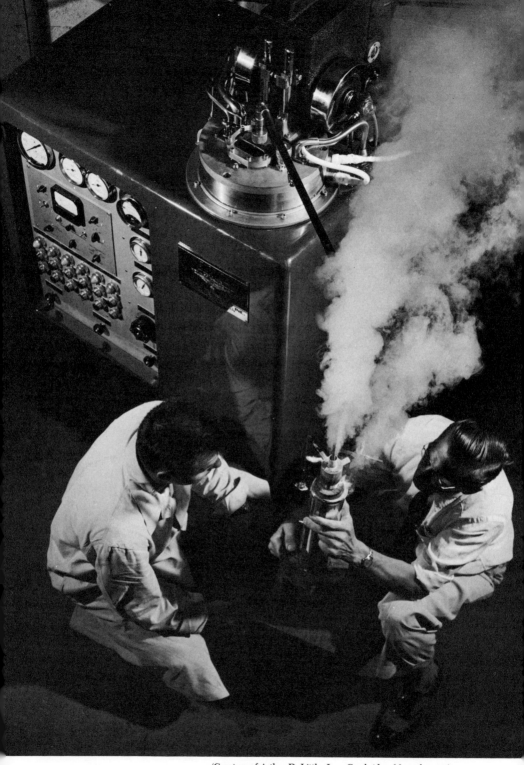

A Collins helium liquefier, showing the transfer of liquid to a glass storage vessel.

know that the power radiated by a body is proportional to the fourth power of its absolute temperature. This means that the heat influx to the inner liquid is reduced about two hundredfold, a reduction of $(77/300)^4$.

A typical storage vessel for liquid helium is shown in the photograph. In essence, it consists of two Dewars, one inside the other, the space between them being filled with liquid nitrogen. Such a Dewar contains from 25 to 50 liters of helium, and has an evaporation rate of about 80 cc of liquid per day. We can gauge how small the associated heat input may be from the fact that an equal amount of heat would melt only a tiny ice cube about one half inch to each side. It is

Double Dewar vessels especially designed for storing liquid helium.

possible, therefore, to store liquid helium for many weeks without any appreciable loss by evaporation.

The term *cryostat*, from the Greek *kryos* meaning "icy cold," has come to be used for any vessel in which low temperature experiments are conducted. For many experiments, it is only necessary to work below the boiling point of a suitable refrigerant. In this case, the cryostat consists of a Dewar system connected to a pump and a suitable device for pressure measurement. By maintaining the pressure above the liquid at a predetermined value, it is possible to obtain a considerable range of temperatures. As we will see later, a knowledge of the vapor pressure-temperature relationship for the liquid gas being used enables us to measure the temperature from the vapor pressure reading.

When experiments are carried out at temperatures below those of liquid hydrogen, it is necessary to use a double Dewar system for the same reasons we have just discussed. The photograph shows a typical system for operating in the region from about 1°K to 4°K. This clearly demonstrates the double Dewar system and the pumping line for reducing the pressure above the helium bath. The silvering on the Dewars allows us to observe the liquid helium level visually during an experiment. In many installations the helium gas produced by evaporating liquid is conserved in storage cylinders so that it may be reliquefied.

When we use liquid He^3 as a refrigerant to produce temperatures below 1°K, some form of closed system is absolutely necessary. This is because a cubic centimeter of gaseous He^3 costs about ten cents, and a typical installation may require as much as 5000 cc of gas to provide enough liquid for an experiment. In order to reach temperatures as low as 0.3°K, it is important to maintain a very low heat influx to the He^3 bath. This is usually done by condensing the He^3 into a small can located in an evacuated enclosure surrounded by liquid He^4 at a temperature of about 1°K. The apparatus shown in the diagram is typical. In use, an outer jacket surrounds the inner container, and the space between the two is evacuated to a pressure of about 10^{-7} mm of mercury, to prevent gas conduction from the outer bath of He^4. The schematic diagram (page 151) shows how the gas from the evaporating liquid is stored for reuse. The pump is very carefully sealed to prevent gas leakage.

(Westinghouse Research Laboratories.)

A typical laboratory installation of a double Dewar system for operating at temperatures in the region of 1°K to 4°K.

So far, we have been considering refrigeration by means of liquefied gases, capable of producing temperatures down to about 0.3°K. However, there are numerous interesting phenomena that occur only below this temperature. In order to obtain significantly lower temperatures, it is necessary to use *adiabatic demagnetization*. This technique was first suggested by P. Debye and W. F. Giauque, quite independently, and is sometimes referred to as the Giauque-Debye Method. It involves the use of a *paramagnetic salt* as a refrigerant. A paramagnetic salt is some chemical whose ions are weakly magnetic. One of those commonly used is iron alum ($FeSO_4 \cdot Al_2(SO_3) \cdot 6H_2O$). The iron ions in this salt are slightly magnetic, behaving as magnets but far less strongly than they do in metallic iron.

Suppose we cool such a paramagnetic salt down to liquid helium temperatures, so that there is virtually no thermal energy in the crystal, and then apply a strong magnetic field. The ions, being little magnets, tend to align themselves with their resultant electronic spins parallel to this field. We now thermally isolate the salt, and then

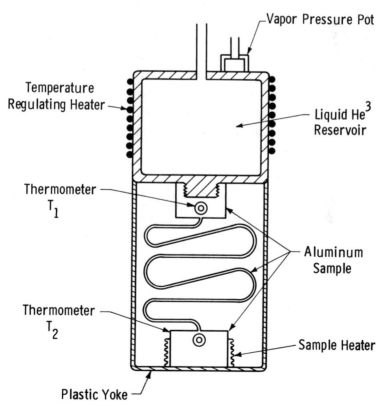

Schematic drawing of a typical He^3 thermal conductivity apparatus. When in use, the inner part shown here is enclosed in an outer jacket, and the space between the two is evacuated, as explained in the text.

remove the magnetic field. As soon as the field is removed, the spins of the ions become disordered again, a process that requires energy. Since the salt is thermally isolated, however, this energy can come only from its *thermal* energy; the salt cools down.

The entropy-temperature diagram in Fig. 6.4 indicates this process graphically. In zero field, the *entropy* of the salt is entirely magnetic, by which we mean that it is essentially a measure of the disorder of the spins of the paramagnetic ions. When the magnetic field is applied, the spins tend to align themselves parallel to the field, and the spin system has a tendency to become more ordered; consequently, there is a *decrease* in the entropy of the system. The magnetization process has been performed at constant temperature, and hence we go from a point A to one such as B in Fig. 6.4. Now, when we thermally isolate the system and demagnetize, there can be no change in entropy; we then proceed to point C on the zero field entropy curve. It is obvious that there will be a great change in the temperature of the salt, provided we are in a region where the spin entropy is a rapidly changing function of temperature. In fact, if we start at 1°K in an initial field of 10,000 gauss, for example, it is very easy to reach about 0.001°K. The diagrammatic sketch in Fig. 6.5 shows the demagnetization procedure. The paramagnetic salt is contained in a can sur-

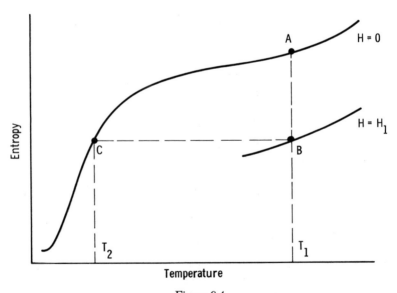

Figure 6.4

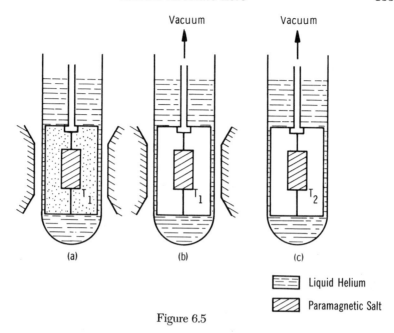

Figure 6.5

rounded by liquid helium at about 1°K, and situated between the poles of an electromagnet. Initially the can is filled with helium gas to give a good thermal contact between the salt and the helium bath. Now the field is applied, as in Fig. 6.5a. The gas is then pumped out, which thermally isolates the salt, as in Fig. 6.5b. The field is removed and the salt cools down (Fig. 6.5c).

By attaching metal vanes to the salt, we can cool other substances, such as metals, to temperatures as low as .01°K. Naturally, the apparatus for demagnetization is actually much more complicated than might be imagined from this description.

For complex reasons, which we need not consider here, the lower limit of temperature attainable by the technique of demagnetization of paramagnetic salts is about 0.001°K. To achieve still lower temperatures, it is necessary to use the technique of *nuclear* demagnetization. In this process, we employ the nuclear spins of the ions of a *metal* to produce a cooling effect. We can again use the diagram in Fig. 6.4, but with the understanding that the entropy now is that of the *nuclear* spins. Again we start from an initial temperature T_1 and apply a magnetic field, partly aligning the nuclear spins. During this process, heat is given off, and is conducted away. The metal is then thermally isolated and the magnetic field is removed; the spins become randomly oriented and the temperature of the metal becomes T_2.

In order for a significant cooling effect to occur, it is necessary that the application of a magnetic field H produce an appreciable reduction in the entropy of the nuclear spins. The amount of orientation can be measured by the ratio of the energy of the spin in the field to the thermal energy, that is, by the ratio $\mu H/kT$, where μ is the strength of the little magnet. For an appreciable change in entropy, we must have

$$\mu H/kT \sim 1. \tag{6.1}$$

Now, for a typical *electron* spin, the condition of Eq. 6.1 is satisfied by relatively small fields, of the order of 10,000 gauss. For *nuclear* spins, however, the factor μ is about 1000 times smaller. In order to produce an appreciable cooling in this case, H/T must be about 1000 times larger than in the previous case. However, since the maximum value of H conveniently obtainable is about 10^5 gauss, it is necessary to start from a much lower temperature, of the order of $0.01°$K. To achieve this, we use ordinary adiabatic demagnetization to precool the metal. With this technique, it is possible to produce temperatures as low as *one-millionth* of a degree absolute.

In any experiment involving low temperatures, it is necessary to have some accurate means of measuring the temperature itself. The basis of all thermometry is the *gas thermometer*. Essentially this thermometer consists of a bulb containing gas under pressure, which is connected by a fine capillary to a pressure gauge. Clearly, as the temperature of the bulb is changed, the gas pressure will also change, causing the gauge reading to alter. By immersing the bulb in baths of known temperature, the gauge can be calibrated, in principle, to read directly in degrees absolute.

The gas thermometer's usefulness depends on the fact that a perfect gas obeys the relation

$$pV = aT, \tag{6.2}$$

where T is the absolute temperature, and a is constant for a given mass of gas. Now, suppose we have a vessel of fixed *volume*, containing an ideal gas, which we place in a bath, such as ice, of known absolute temperature T_1, and we let P_1 be the pressure of gas at this temperature. Let's further suppose that we now place the container in contact with the body whose temperature T_2 we wish to measure, and the pressure reading is P_2. Since the volume of gas is constant, V, from Eq. 6.2 we have

$$P_1 V = aT_1; \qquad P_2 V = aT_2,$$

and dividing these two equations and transposing, we obtain

$$T_2 = T_1 \frac{P_2}{P_1}. \tag{6.3}$$

Thus, knowing all the quantities on the right-hand side of Eq. 6.3, we can find T_2, the absolute temperature of the unknown body. A gas thermometer based on this principle is called a *constant volume* gas thermometer. In an exactly analogous fashion, we can construct a thermometer in which the pressure is left fixed; this is a *constant pressure* thermometer.

Now, in actuality, neither of these thermometers is as simple as we might suppose from the description. A typical constant volume gas thermometer differs from that described in two respects:

First, the gas used in the thermometer is *not* a perfect gas.

Second, the pressure indicator and the tube, leading to the gas thermometer bulb, have a finite volume, which is *not* at the temperature being measured.

However, these difficulties can be overcome. The first effect is minimized by using a gas at fairly low pressure, where the deviations from the perfect gas law are small and can be quite accurately calculated. The second effect is reduced by keeping "dead space" of the capillary and gauge as small as possible; corrections for this dead space can then also be determined quite accurately.

Although the gas thermometer is an *absolute* instrument, it is not very convenient to use. For this reason, it is customary to employ it only as a standard, using other more flexible thermometers in everyday experiments. These are of four main types: resistance thermometers, thermocouples, vapor-pressure thermometers, and magnetic thermometers.

RESISTANCE THERMOMETERS

It is well known that the electrical resistance of a metal changes with temperature. The reason for this is that the electrons in a metal

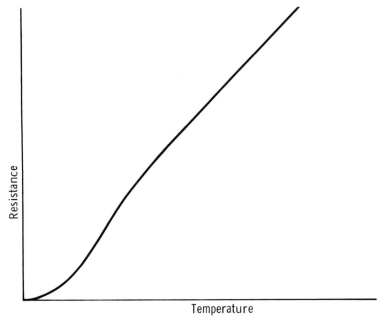

Figure 6.6

are scattered as a result of the vibrations of the atoms. As the temperature of the metal is raised, the atoms vibrate more and more, the
electrons are scattered more strongly, and the resistance of the metal
increases. Similarly, as the temperature is lowered, the resistance is
lowered. In general, the resistance of a *well-annealed* sample of *pure
metal* is a quite reproducible function of temperature, and has the
general form shown in Fig. 6.6. Therefore, if we can measure the
resistance of a suitable coil of metal wire, its temperature can be
determined, and hence also the temperature of the body with which
it is in contact. This is the basic principle of the resistance thermometer. Usually a coil of platinum wire is used, which has first been carefully annealed, then wound in a strain-free manner on a mica form. A
typical thermometer of this kind can measure temperatures down to
about $20°$K with an accuracy of better than $0.001°$K. Below this temperature, however, the sensitivity of the platinum resistance thermometer becomes quite poor, since the change of resistance with temperature is very small. Therefore, below $20°$K it is customary to employ a
carbon resistance or *germanium* thermometer.

THERMOCOUPLES

If we have two dissimilar metals whose functions are maintained at temperatures T_1 and T_2, as shown in Fig. 6.7, we find that an electromotive force (emf) is generated between the open ends. In particular, if one junction is maintained at 0°C, for example, and the other is maintained at a temperature T, the emf, E, generated by the thermocouple, is a well-defined function of this temperature. This means that the thermocouple can be used as a thermometer. For low temperatures, the most commonly used thermocouple employs copper and constantan wires, the latter being composed of a special alloy of copper and nickel. This type of thermocouple is useful down to about liquid nitrogen temperature, and has a calibration curve that is very reproducible, provided the wire is carefully made. This means that a thermocouple cable can be prepared which gives the temperature of the cold function as a function of the emf generated. Because of this feature and the fact that they are inexpensive, copper-constantan couples are frequently used as secondary thermometers.

Below 77°K, however, copper-constantan couples are not very satisfactory, because their thermo-emf does not change very much with temperature. It is therefore necessary to use special thermocouples, such as copper vs. gold-cobalt, which are quite sensitive even down to liquid helium temperatures. Unlike the copper-constantan couples, however, their calibration curves are rather variable, and each couple must be individually calibrated against a gas thermometer. This somewhat limits their usefulness.

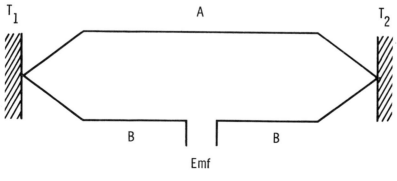

Figure 6.7

VAPOR PRESSURE THERMOMETERS

We all know that water under a pressure of atmosphere boils at exactly 100°C, and that as the pressure is reduced, the boiling point decreases in a known way. For example, on Mount Everest water will boil at about 80°C. In a similar way, the boiling points of the gases at a pressure of one atmosphere are well known. Furthermore, their boiling points at reduced pressure are known as a function of temperature and are compiled in what are known as *vapor pressure tables*. Thus, if we know the vapor pressure above a gas, we can immediately find its temperature, and the temperature of the objects in thermal contact with it. To avoid errors due to convection, among other things, it is usual to employ some form of *vapor pressure thermometer* to determine the temperature of a body immersed in the liquefied gas. This consists of a small bulb, containing the condensed gas, situated

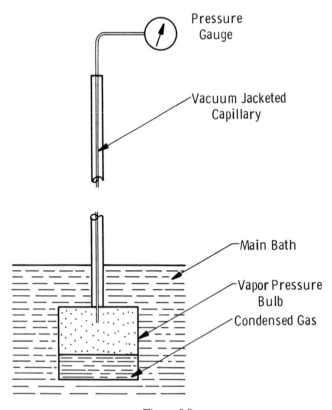

Figure 6.8

near the body and connected to a pressure-measuring device by means of a vacuum-jacketed tube. The latter prevents undesired thermal contact between the gas in the thermometer and the remainder of the bath. In this way we insure that we are, in fact, measuring the bath temperature *at the body* and not at some arbitrary part of the bath, which can be at quite a different temperature because of convection currents. A diagram of a vapor pressure thermometer is shown in Fig. 6.8.

MAGNETIC THERMOMETERS

Below 1°K, the vapor pressure of all gases becomes immeasurably small. The thermocouple and resistance thermometers alike are unusable, because neither the thermo-emf nor the resistance of a wire varies with temperature in this region. It is therefore necessary to devise some other form of thermometer. For use in this low temperature region, the magnetic thermometer has been developed. There are two types, one involving the spins of paramagnetic ions and the other involving the spins of metallic nuclei.

The first of these employs paramagnetic salts, discussed previously. As we mentioned, these contain magnetic ions that act like miniature bar magnets when in the presence of a magnetic field, and tend to line up *parallel* to the field. This tendency to alignment is opposed by the thermal motion of the magnets, and thus the *net moment* of the salt along the direction of the field, which is a measure of the degree of alignment, is a function of temperature. Experimentally, it proves more convenient to measure the susceptibility, χ, of a paramagnetic salt, rather than its moment. This is defined as the ratio of the increment of moment M, divided by the increment in field H, at a given temperature, thus

$$\chi = \frac{\Delta M}{\Delta H} \tag{6.4}$$

or, strictly speaking, $\chi = dM/dH$. It can be shown quite generally that, over a wide range of temperature, susceptibility of a paramagnetic salt follows the Curie-Weiss law, which is named for its discoverers;

$$\chi = \frac{a}{T - \Delta}, \tag{6.5}$$

where a and Δ are constants for a given salt, and T is the absolute temperature. A given salt may be calibrated above $1°K$ by measuring its susceptibility as a function of the temperature, the temperature being obtained from the vapor pressure tables for liquid helium. In this way we can obtain a and Δ very simply, by plotting $1/\chi$ vs. T. The graph

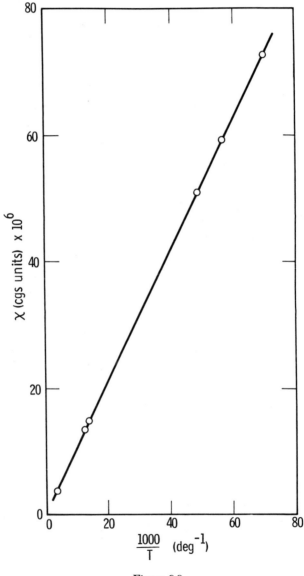

Figure 6.9

for this should be a straight line. Such a plot for copper potassium sulfate is shown in Fig. 6.9. Knowing a and Δ, it is easy to obtain the temperature *below* 1°K by measuring χ at that temperature and using the relation of Eq. 6.5. At sufficiently low temperatures, the Curie-Weiss law actually is no longer obeyed, because the interactions between the ions becomes too large. However, we can still write the susceptibility in the form

$$\chi = \frac{a}{T^* - \Delta}, \qquad (6.6)$$

where T^* is now called a *magnetic* temperature and is *no longer* equal to the absolute temperature. It is possible, however, to find the relation between T and T^*, so that the paramagnetic thermometer is useful down to temperatures as low as 0.001°K.

Beyond this point, we can use the *nuclear* spin susceptibility as a thermometer. It can be shown that in this case the constant Δ is zero, and that a is calculable from the known nuclear moment of the metal ions. In this way we can calculate T directly from the known nuclear susceptibility. Such measurements can extend the temperature scale down to values as low as one-millionth of a degree absolute.

SPECIFIC HEATS

Although there are innumerable interesting phenomena that occur at low temperatures, we are going to confine our present discussion to the following low temperature properties of solids: specific heats, superconductivity, and superfluidity.

As explained in Chapter Three, Eq. 3.40, classical theory predicts that atoms vibrating in a solid should each have an energy kT per degree of freedom, k being the Boltzmann constant and T the absolute temperature. Therefore, since each atom has three translational degrees of freedom (that is, it can move independently in three mutually perpendicular directions), the energy of the solid per mole is

$$E = 3NkT, \qquad (6.7)$$

where N is Avagadro's number. Let's consider now the heat ΔQ required to raise the temperature of the solid at constant volume by an amount ΔT. Clearly, we have

$$\Delta Q = \Delta E = 3Nk\Delta T.$$

Thus, dividing by ΔT, we have

$$C_v = \frac{\Delta Q}{\Delta T} = 3Nk, \qquad (6.8)$$

where C_v is called the *molar specific heat of solid at constant volume*. Now, we know that $Nk = R$, where R is the gas constant, so that Eq. 6.8 may be written

$$C_v = 3R. \qquad (6.9)$$

Thus, the molar specific heat of a solid is constant and is approximately 6 calorie/degree. This law was first observed experimentally by Dulong and Petit, and is named for them.

Early measurements of the specific heats of solids at low temperatures showed that Dulong and Petit's law was no longer obeyed, and that, in fact, the variation of C_v with temperature was of the general form shown in Fig. 6.10. It was Albert Einstein who showed that this deviation from classical theory could be explained in terms of the *quantum theory*, newly formulated at that time. This demonstration was one of the most spectacular successes of this theory. Einstein showed that by treating the system as an assembly of *harmonic oscillators*, each having a characteristic frequency of oscillation ν_E, the

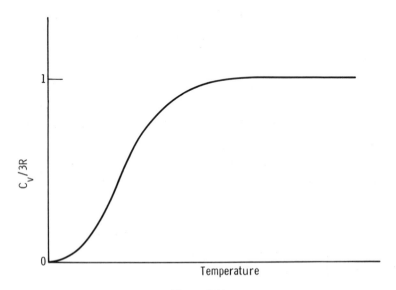

Figure 6.10

general shape of the curve is reproduced. The classical value of $3R$ is attained only when thermal energy kT is considerably in excess of the oscillator energy $h\nu_E$, that is, when

$$kT \gg h\nu_E$$

or, in other words,

$$T \gg h\nu_E/k. \tag{6.10}$$

The quantity on the right-hand side of Eq. 6.10 defines a temperature, which we call the *Einstein characteristic temperature* of the solid, $\theta_E = h\nu_E/k$. The condition for the specific heat of a solid to obtain its classical value is thus $T \gg \theta_E$.

At *very low* temperatures, $T \ll \theta_E$, the Einstein theory of specific heat predicted that the specific heat should drop off exponentially, that is,

$$C \sim e^{-\theta_E/T}. \tag{6.11}$$

Heat capacity measurements at liquid hydrogen and liquid helium temperatures showed, however, that at sufficiently low temperatures

$$C \sim T^3, \tag{6.12}$$

that is, the specific heat did not disappear as fast as was predicted by the Einstein formula. This difficulty was solved by Peter Debye, who showed that the form of Eq. 6.12 was obtained if, instead of assuming a single oscillator frequency, the oscillators had frequencies varying from zero up to a maximum value ν_D. As before, each solid would have a characteristic value of this frequency, and a corresponding *Debye temperature*, defined by the equation

$$\theta_D = h\nu_D/k. \tag{6.13}$$

The specific heat of a solid could then be written in the form

$$C_v = 3Rf_D(\theta/T), \tag{6.14}$$

where $f_D(\theta/T)$ is a *universal* function of the so-called reduced temperature T/θ. This theory has been very successful in predicting the low temperature *vibrational* specific heat of solids. Some idea of this success may be obtained from Fig. 6.11, which shows $C/3R$ plotted as a function of T/θ for aluminum and copper. The values of Debye temperature used in obtaining this plot are shown, and it will be seen

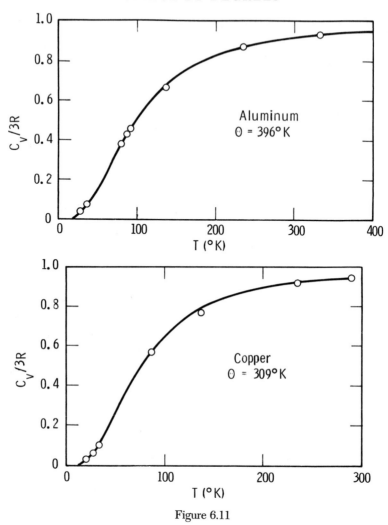

Figure 6.11

that the fit of the theoretical $f_D(T/\theta)$ to the experimental points is very good.

At liquid helium temperatures, however, it was noticed that although Eq. 6.12 fitted the specific heat data for insulating solids, it did not fit that for metals at all well. It was found that in this case the specific heat at low temperatures was of the form

$$C = \gamma T + aT^3. \tag{6.15}$$

Before long it was realized that this additional *linear* term came from the specific heat of the *conduction electrons* in the metal.

Drude was the first to propose that the conduction electrons in a metal could be regarded as forming a sort of gas. Initially this gas was treated as a classical assembly of particles. After the advent of quantum mechanics, however, it was realized by Sommerfeld that such an assembly must obey Fermi-Dirac statistics. As we saw in Chapter Five, this means that only two electrons, each of opposite spin, can occupy a given energy state. At absolute zero, all energies up to a given energy are occupied. This is known as the *Fermi energy*, E_0; beyond this, all states are empty. As the temperature T is raised, however, those states lying approximately in the region kT of the Fermi energy are repopulated. Fig. 6.12 shows the probability of occupation of energy levels at absolute zero and at some finite temperature T.

Only those electrons lying in this narrow region of energy can be excited, and these constitute a fraction, kT/E_0, of the total. If all the electrons could participate, we would have an associated specific heat of $3Nk$, N being the total number of electrons. Thus, the actual electronic specific heat would be

$$C_E = 3Nk(kT/E_0), \tag{6.16}$$

that is, the electronic heat capacity should be *linear* in temperature.

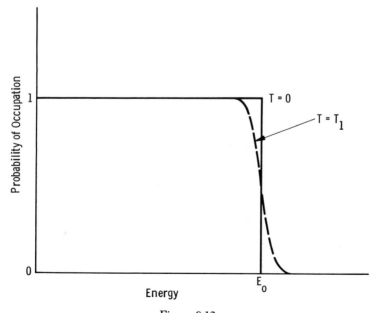

Figure 6.12

Actually, the coefficient γ of this linear term is not given exactly by Eq. 6.16; for an assembly of free electrons, the expression for γ is

$$\gamma = (\pi^2/3)(Nk^2/E_0). \tag{6.17}$$

Measurements of the coefficient γ for metals can give valuable information about their electronic structure.

SUPERCONDUCTIVITY

As we have already mentioned earlier in this discussion, the electrical resistance of a metal at high temperatures is caused by the lattice vibrations scattering the conduction electrons. As the temperature is decreased, the amplitude of these vibrations also decreases, so that the electrons are no longer as strongly scattered, and the electrical resistance decreases. The general form of the graph of the electrical resistance of a metal vs. temperature is shown in Fig. 6.6. As we approach absolute zero, the electrical resistance of a very pure metal becomes extremely small, and is essentially independent of temperature. In this temperature range, its conductivity is no longer limited by the lattice scattering, but by the impurities which it contains. It is not uncommon for the *residual resistance* of a metal of exceptional purity to be,

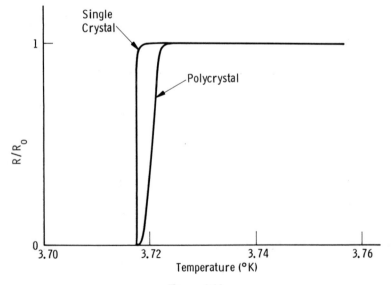

Figure 6.13

at absolute zero, as much as one ten-thousandth of its value at room temperature. However, it is important to understand that the conductivity is still *finite*.

Very soon after liquid helium was first made, measurements were obtained of the electrical resistance of pure mercury at very low temperatures. It was found that at temperatures just below the boiling point of helium, contrary to the case of normal metals, the resistance of mercury becomes *immeasurably small*. A new property had been discovered, and it was called *superconductivity*. It has since been found that a number of metals and alloys have this same property.

For a pure metal, free of any strain, the transition from the normal to superconducting state takes place in a discontinuous fashion at a characteristic temperature, known as the transition temperature T_c. A typical transition curve for tin is shown in Fig. 6.13. Transition temperatures for superconductors cover a wide range, as may be seen from Table 6.B. The highest value yet recorded is for the compound Nb_3N, which has a transition temperature of $18°K$.

The ability of superconductors to conduct electricity without any resistance is graphically demonstrated in the accompanying photo. In this experiment, two lead rings have been cooled down below their transition temperature, and currents induced in them by a magnet. The lead ball is supported in the magnetic field produced by these currents. There is no detectable change in this field as long as the rings are kept superconducting, showing that the current is, indeed, constant and that each ring has zero electrical resistance. Experiments have been carried out in which currents of *hundreds* of amperes have been kept flowing for periods of *several weeks*, without any detectable change!

Shortly after the discovery of the superconductivity of mercury, it was found that when a sufficiently large magnetic field was applied,

TABLE 6.B

Material	H_0 (oersted)	T_c (°K)	Material	H_0 (oersted)	T_c (°K)
Zn	53	0.89	Nb	2600	9.22
Sn	305	3.69	Nb_3Zr	2500	10.9
Hg	413	4.12	Nb_3Sn	5000	18.1
Pb	805	7.26			

(Courtesy of Arthur D. Little, Inc., Cambridge, Massachusetts.)

A hollow lead ball is supported by the magnetic field of two superconducting lead rings with induced persistent currents of opposite direction. This experiment is performed at 4.2°K by cooling in a liquid helium bath.

the mercury's superconductivity was destroyed. This came to be known as the *critical* magnetic field, and it was found to vary very nearly in a parabolic fashion with temperature, as shown in Fig. 6.14. Later work demonstrated that the critical field H_c of any superconductor obeys a similar relation, and can be written as

$$H_c = H_0(1 - T^2/T_c^2). \qquad (6.18)$$

In this equation, T_c is the transition temperature, and H_0 is a constant characteristic of the superconductor. The values of H_0 for various superconductors are given in Table 6.B, which shows that in the case of some alloys, the limiting value of the critical field can exceed many thousands of oersted. This has important technical implications, as we shall see later.

Superconductors possess another equally interesting magnetic property. Below their critical field, the value of the magnetic induction B within them is zero. This is known as the *Meissner effect*, which can be very graphically demonstrated by the following experiment. A thin cylinder of a superconductor is wound with a closely fitting coil of wire, connected to the coils of a ballistic galvanometer. An external field H is then applied, and quickly reversed. For a normal metal, this

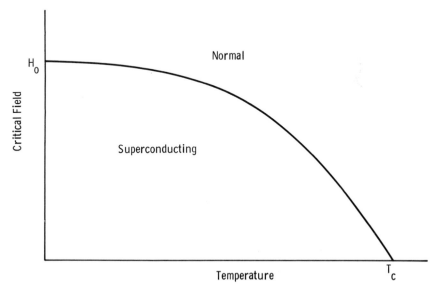

Figure 6.14

field reversal would cause a deflection of the galvanometer, proportional to the flux through the secondary coil, and we would expect to obtain a galvanometer deflection which is linear in the field H, as shown by the dotted line in Fig. 6.15. For a superconductor, however, we obtain zero deflection, until the critical field H_c is reached, showing that the magnetic induction is, indeed, zero. In other words, the superconductor acts like a perfect *diamagnet,* which is graphically demonstrated by the experiment shown in the photograph. Here we see a small bar magnet floating above a lead dish. The weight of the magnet is entirely supported by the repulsive force due to the diamagnetism of the superconducting lead dish! This property, too, has important technological applications.

In this rather brief review of superconductivity, another property should be mentioned: the electronic specific heat of a superconductor is not linear, but rather, at low temperatures obeys an *exponential* temperature dependence,

$$C_{es} \sim \exp\left(-bT_c/T\right), \tag{6.19}$$

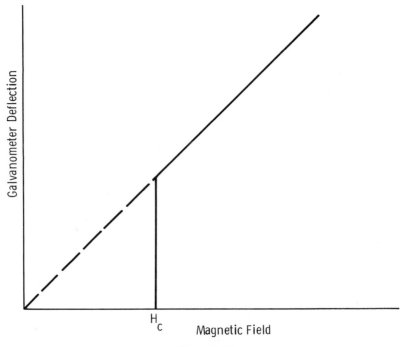

Figure 6.15

(Courtesy of Arthur D. Little, Inc., Cambridge, Massachusetts.)

A bar magnet floats on a magnetic field above a superconducting lead bowl, as described in the text.

where b is a constant. This unusual property results from the fact that in a superconductor the probability of occupation of the energy levels at absolute zero and at temperature T is as shown in Fig. 6.16. It can be seen that near the Fermi level E_0 there is an energy gap of magni-

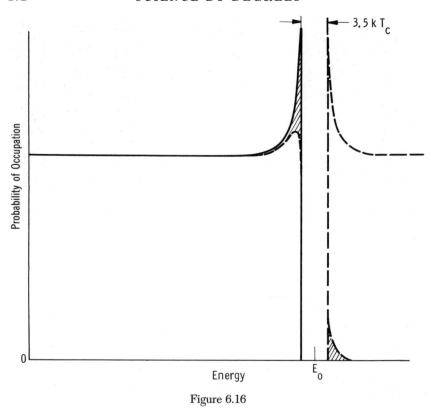

Figure 6.16

tude $3.5kT_c$. The excitation of particles across this gap at higher temperatures (see shaded area) is responsible for the exponential electronic specific heat.

SUPERFLUIDITY

In experimenting with liquid helium, shortly after it was first produced, it was noticed that many of its properties changed discontinuously at about $2.17°K$. Measurements of its specific heat, in particular, showed a striking anomaly, as may be seen in Fig. 6.17. Such a curve is quite similar to the specific heat anomalies associated with a *phase transition,* such as those discussed previously. It was soon discovered that the liquid helium anomaly was also associated with a phase change. The phase below the transition temperature was designated *helium II,* to distinguish it from the *helium I* phase which existed above the transition temperature.

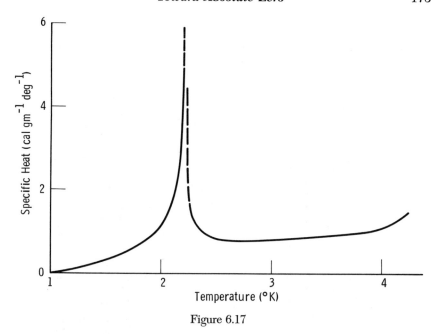

Figure 6.17

The properties of liquid helium II proved quite unusual. For example, when a beaker is immersed in liquid helium II, so that the level inside the beaker is initially lower than that of the liquid outside, the beaker gradually fills, until both levels are the same. Again, if a beaker of liquid helium II is raised above the surface of the liquid, it gradually empties. This draining process is clearly visible in the photo.

Another example of the peculiar nature of liquid helium II is demonstrated by the *fountain effect* shown in the photograph. Here we have a tube, whose lower end is tightly packed with emery powder. In spite of this dense obstruction, when light is allowed to fall on the emery powder, a jet of liquid helium is projected through it, rising several centimeters into the air. The fact that it can flow with such relative ease through the fine orifices of the emery powder shows that liquid helium II possesses an incredibly low viscosity. This *superfluidity* is analogous, in many ways, to superconductivity.

It may help in understanding the phenomenon of superfluidity if we consider helium II as an example of a *Bose-Einstein liquid,* that is, a condensed assembly of helium atoms which obey Bose-Einstein statistics. We mentioned in Chapter Five that for particles obeying such statistics, there is no limit to the number that can occupy any energy

(Courtesy of Arthur D. Little, Inc., Cambridge, Massachusetts.)

Superfluid helium II creeping over the sides of a small test tube and dripping off the bottom into the larger volume of helium II, as explained in the text.

level. In particular, it can be shown that there is a certain *critical temperature* at which all particles can condense into a zero energy state. Because of the fact that there can be no momentum transfer between particles in this state, such a liquid would be, in fact, a super-

(Courtesy of Arthur D. Little, Inc., Cambridge, Massachusetts.)

The superfluidity of liquid helium II is demonstrated by the "fountain effect" illustrated in this photograph and explained in the text.

fluid with zero viscosity. Moreover, it would also have zero entropy, which would account for the fountain effect. It follows, then, that in the emery powder experiment, when light falls on the powder, the liquid helium II, with zero entropy, *must* flow in to absorb the radiant energy and keep the temperature constant. An interesting point is that the critical temperature of a Bose-Einstein liquid, of liquid helium density, is approximately $2.4°K$, which is astonishingly close to the real transition temperature of $2.17°K$.

The interest in liquefied gases and low temperature techniques is not confined to the research laboratory. There are many practical applications, with new uses being discovered constantly.

The most practical and efficient fuels for rockets have long been the subject of intensive investigation. Liquid oxygen, called LOX, has become a familiar oxidizing agent used in many rockets today. Before long, however, super-rockets will be using liquid hydrogen, with its very high thrust per unit mass. There is a tremendous consumption of liquefied gases in rocket installations, and for this purpose special storage tanks the size of large trailer trucks have been designed. The problem of insulating these tanks has been solved by developing special insulating materials, which obviates the necessity of using a vacuum space, making the tanks far more reliable.

Another application of low temperature techniques has been for liquid-cooled radiation detectors. In all detectors of electromagnetic radiation, the ultimate limiting factor in their sensitivity is the *thermal* or *Nyquist noise*. This results essentially from the fluctuating nature of statistical assemblies, and gives rise to an effective noise voltage, directly proportional to the absolute temperature of the detector. We find that by operating detectors at temperatures of liquid nitrogen or, even better, of liquid helium, the performance is greatly improved. Most detectors in use today are cooled with liquid nitrogen. To accomplish such cooling efficiently in a detector installed in an airplane, for example, it is customary to use a cell cooled by a miniature closed-cycle liquefier. The photograph shows a typical unit for cooling a PbS infrared detector. The actual cooling head weighs somewhat less than one pound, while the whole assembly weighs about forty pounds.

The *maser*, discussed in Chapter Four, is another example of the use of low temperatures to improve the noise figure of radiation detectors. This employs liquid helium. A ruby maser, designed for use in a radio telescope, is shown in one photograph. The dish-shaped object in the other photograph is the parabolic reflector, which directs the electromagnetic radiation to the maser. The maser itself, located at the focus

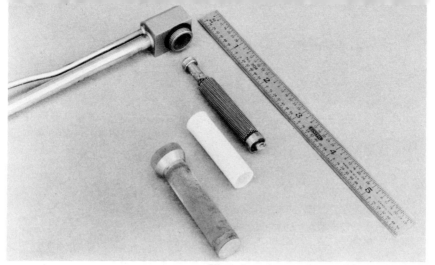

(Westinghouse Aerospace Division, Baltimore, Maryland.)

This miniature closed-cycle liquefier is used in conjunction with nitrogen gas under high pressure to cool a PbS infrared detector. The detector (not shown) is at the tip of the tube on the extreme left.

(Official United States Navy photograph. Used by permission.)

A three-centimeter radiometer with maser preamplifier is shown here mounted on the 50-foot radio telescope at the U.S. Naval Research Laboratory, Washington, D. C.

(Official United States Navy photograph. Used by permission.)

The parabolic reflector of the 50-foot radio telescope at the U.S. Naval Research Laboratory. This reflector directs electromagnetic radiation to the maser located at the focus of the paraboloid.

of the paraboloid, is contained in a small metal Dewar, which keeps liquid helium for about two days before requiring a refill. We get some idea of the efficiency of this Dewar system when we consider that an ordinary picnic thermos flask will keep liquid cool for only a few hours, in spite of the fact that the temperature difference is only about 60°F, as compared to 450°F in the maser system.

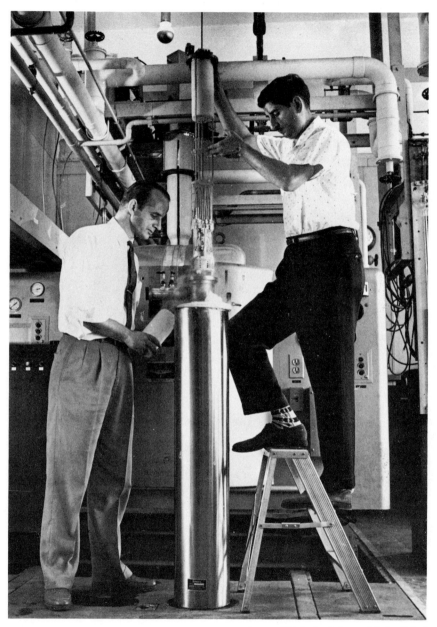

(Westinghouse Research Laboratories.)

In the background is a conventional magnet which can produce a field of about 30 kilogauss in a one-inch gap. The motor generator that powers this magnet occupies a large part of another room. The superconducting magnet in the foreground can achieve a magnetic field intensity of 100,000 gauss and is powered by an automobile battery.

A superconducting magnet is lowered into liquid nitrogen for pre-cooling before being submerged in a helium bath.

There has been a spectacular increase in the number of commercial applications of superconductors. Among these, there are superconducting radiation detectors, memory elements in computers, friction-free gyroscopic devices, and, most recently, superconducting magnets. Interest in the latter has increased greatly because of the discovery that certain alloys, niobium tin (Nb_3Sn) and niobium zirconium (Nb_3Zr), remain superconducting at extremely high currents and fields. Since these alloys can carry such high currents, and can remain superconducting, it is possible to produce a solenoid giving a large field without any power dissipation. This results in a tremendous saving both in the size of magnet to produce a given field, and in the associated power supply. The photograph shows in the background a conventional magnet, which can produce a field of about 30 kilogauss in a one-inch gap. The necessary motor generator for this magnet occupies a good part of another room. The man beside the magnet is holding a superconducting solenoid, which can produce a larger field in a substantial gap, and yet it can be supplied from a couple of automobile storage batteries! So far, superconducting magnets have produced fields up to 100,000 gauss, but there is every reason to believe that in the near future they will produce fields of 200,000 gauss, or even 500,000!

The diamagnetic properties of superconductors are employed to produce friction-free suspensions for gyroscopic devices, such as that shown in the photograph. In this one, the rotor is a very carefully

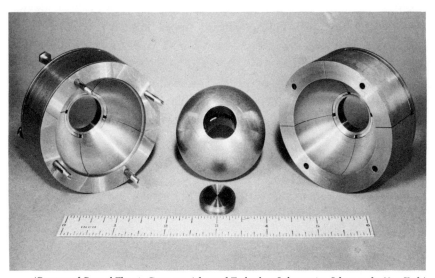

(Courtesy of General Electric Company, Advanced Technology Laboratories, Schenectady, New York.)

Friction-free suspension is achieved in a superconducting gyro with this device. The upper bearing is shown at the left, the lower bearing at the far right. The carefully machined rotor (with the optical mirror in front of it) is shown in the center.

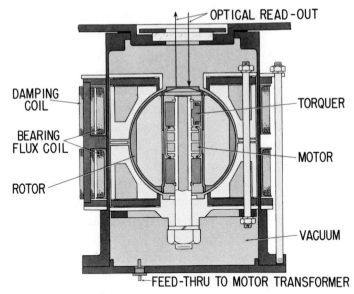

DAMPING COIL

BEARING FLUX COIL

ROTOR

OPTICAL READ-OUT

TORQUER

MOTOR

VACUUM

FEED-THRU TO MOTOR TRANSFORMER

(Courtesy of General Electric Company, Advanced Technology Laboratories, Schenectady, New York.)

Diagram showing the components of the superconducting gyro.

machined lead sphere, suspended between a set of coils designed to produce a suitable magnetic field. Essentially friction-free, a device like this can rotate for months without appreciable loss of speed. This means that far greater accuracy can be achieved in inertial navigation systems and gyrocompasses.

These are only a very few of the possible applications of low temperatures. The next decade will see this dynamic field of physics gain even more importance, as new applications are found and fascinating new devices are produced.

7

More and More Degrees

LOOKING AT THE SUN makes us acutely aware that there are much higher temperatures in nature than we have considered so far. We can tell, even without elaborate instruments, that the sun's temperature is much higher than that of an incandescent lamp filament, which is about 3200°K. More precise measurements indicate that the effective surface temperature of the sun is approximately 5700°K.

If we look carefully at the stars at night, we discover that their colors differ appreciably. Although this is not necessarily because of differences in surface temperatures alone, the cooler stars, such as Betelgeuse in the constellation Orion, are generally reddish in color and may have surface temperatures as low as 2500°K. Orion also includes some extremely hot stars, Rigel and Bellatrix, and especially the primary light sources of the Orion nebula. Some surface temperatures approach 100,000°K. (See Fig. 7.1.)

Can temperatures of a similar magnitude be produced on earth? The answer is a qualified yes, because extremely high temperatures occur in the explosion of an atomic bomb, for example, and also in certain types of electrical discharges. But the operation of most such devices is limited to a fraction of a second, in contrast to the millions of years the stars maintain their temperatures. Systems that operate at such high

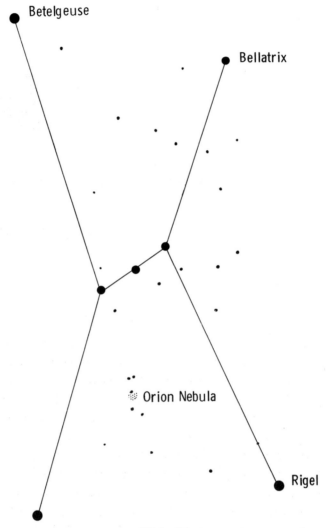

Figure 7.1

temperatures on a continuous basis should be distinguished from those that do not.

Among the first group, an electric discharge was developed a number of years ago in Germany for the specific purpose of reaching an upper limit in electric arcs. A drawing of the apparatus is shown in Fig. 7.2. Temperatures of more than $50,000°$K were measured. Considerably higher temperatures—$200,000$ to $300,000°$K—have been observed recently in a vacuum arc at the Oak Ridge Laboratory. The

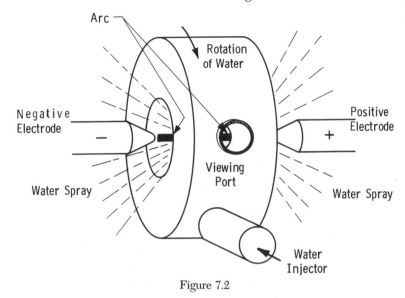

Figure 7.2

photograph shows that arc in operation. It was developed in connection with a nuclear fusion device called *DCX*.

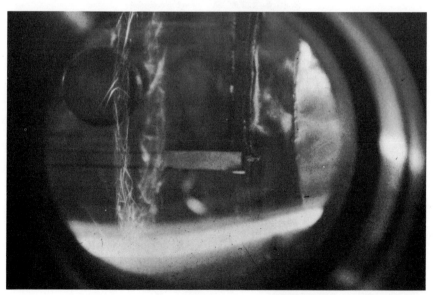

Arc discharge and ion confinement in the DCX, a nuclear fusion device.

By far the most spectacular example of a discontinuous device is the atom bomb, potentially a very promising means of studying extremely high temperatures. The temperature history of such a bomb is shown in Fig. 7.3.

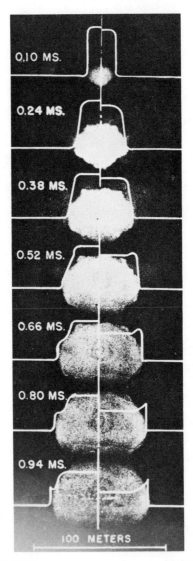

TEMPERATURE   PRESSURE

Figure 7.3

(Courtesy of University of California Radiation Laboratory at Livermore.)

An experimental apparatus, called a "Three-stage Toy Top," at Livermore. Plasma, injected into the large chamber from ion sources at the right, is partially compressed when coils around this chamber are energized. The plasma is then transferred successively to the second and third chambers. Final compression is effected when the coils of the third chamber at the left are energized. Magnetic mirrors check the loss of plasma out of the ends of the tube.

Project Sherwood of the United States Atomic Energy Commission, dedicated to the production of controlled nuclear fusion, needs temperatures of the order of one hundred million degrees for the successful harnessing of thermonuclear reactions. One of their experimental devices at Los Alamos, New Mexico—called *Scylla*—has produced a temperature of thirty million degrees, albeit at low pressure and only for a few microseconds. Another machine at the Livermore Laboratories has achieved temperatures of similar magnitude for over a millisecond.

Going up in temperature above the 2000°K of ordinary fires on

earth, we may perhaps think that we encounter a strange and different world. And yet when we look at the universe as a whole, and particularly at the vast amount of matter concentrated in the stars, by far
the most common temperatures are in the millions of degrees, not in
the hundreds. It becomes obvious that we should consider our own
modest temperatures on earth as the exception rather than the rule.

A question immediately arises in this connection. In what state is
matter at such high temperatures? So far, we have been dealing with
three states of matter: solids, liquids, and gases. We have seen that
when the temperature is raised sufficiently high, all materials will
eventually become gases. Is this, then, the ultimate state to which
matter can go?

In order to answer this question, we must look back at the familiar
three states to see what differentiates them. In the solid state, the
average position of each atom or molecule is rigidly fixed with respect
to its neighbors. In the liquid state, we do not find such restrictions.
The molecules are still interacting fairly strongly with their neighbors,
but they can now slip and slide along each other. We have broken down
the barrier of the large form, the crystal. At best, we now have a drop-
let. In the next state, the gaseous, even more barriers are eliminated.
There is no longer any appreciable cohesion between neighbors. In an
ideal gas, each molecule is completely free.

But how about the internal structure of these particles? So far, the
electrons and nuclei in the molecule or atom have stayed together in
reasonably fixed positions, at least as far as the effects of heat are concerned. Up to now we considered them as units, regardless of any
internal phenomena. The reason for this is the following: At each temperature, we have available a certain amount of energy, which is used
to disrupt the natural binding that exists between particles. At low
temperatures, only little energy is present, so that only relatively weak
binding energies can be overcome successfully. But as we reach temperatures on the order of 3000°K, the heat energy approaches the
binding energy of the electrons themselves. It becomes possible to
separate from the molecule first one and then more than one electron,
so that we form two kinds of gases, one charged electrically negative,
the other one positive. In most cases, the negatively charged gas consists only of free electrons, while the positively charged gas consists of
what remains of the atom or molecule. This remainder is called *ion.*

We have now obtained a new state of matter, the fourth state, called *plasma*, in which ions and electrons exist separately side by side.

As the temperature is raised higher and higher, the heat energy becomes sufficiently great to eject even the innermost electrons of the heavy nuclei. The *plasma state* can be said to extend up to a temperature at which nothing is left but bare atomic nuclei and free electrons. For the hydrogen atom, which contains just one electron—and therefore only one electron has to be removed to obtain the bare nucleus—this occurs at temperatures on the order of 15,000°K. For the heaviest nuclei, uranium for example, which normally has 92 electrons, the removal of all electrons calls for a temperature of 10^9 degrees Kelvin. This, then, is the range of the plasma state—the fourth state of matter.

Having ventured this far, the question naturally arises whether additional states can be defined along similar lines. This is indeed possible, as we shall see. We will refer to them, whatever their characteristics, by additional numbers—five, six, and so on—although present conventions in the field of high temperature physics do not explicitly use this nomenclature.

What might the *fifth* state of matter be? In a plasma, heat energy associated with temperature is sufficient to eject electrons from their orbits, but it cannot affect the atomic nuclei themselves. Now, as we continue to increase the temperature, eventually we reach the binding energy of protons and neutrons inside the nuclei. We are approaching nuclear temperature, the fifth state of matter, which is found within the atomic nuclei. If this were to be measured in degrees, we would be up to 10^{11}. Could we raise matter in bulk to such temperatures, the atomic nuclei would "melt" into a sea of protons and neutrons.

Shall we attempt a sixth state of matter? Can we reach temperatures at which the protons and neutrons themselves can no longer hold together? Indeed, there is evidence in cosmic rays and in the huge modern synchrotrons that protons and neutrons, when supplied with sufficiently high energies, yield still more elementary units, called *mesons*. Furthermore, no law has yet been discovered in physics which prohibits us from imagining a temperature of a system of mesons in thermal equilibrium! This would mean temperatures of 10^{13} degrees Kelvin.

This is as far as speculation goes in science at the present time. Mesons have not been studied enough, as yet, to make further predictions. But perhaps some day in the future, when we have additional experience with subnuclear matter, it will be possible to contemplate yet more states of matter.

PLASMAS

All matter in the form to which we are accustomed on earth gradually acquires the characteristics of the fourth state of matter, plasma, as the temperature is increased above a few thousand degrees. We might assume that, as ions are formed by energetic collisions at a fixed temperature and pressure, the entire mass of gas would soon be ionized. But this is not the case. Whenever an ion meets a free electron, there is a certain probability that the two will recombine into an electrically neutral atom, as it was originally, thus tending to reduce the total number of ions. In effect, equilibrium is attained for which, at any given temperature, the rate of ion formation equals the rate of recombination, leaving the gas as a whole with a constant percentage of ions.

Calculation of the equilibrium condition for thermal ionization can be done on the basis of the reaction between an atom (A) and its ion (A^+) as illustrated by the equation

$$(A) + E_i \rightleftharpoons (A^+) + e^-,$$

where e^- stands for electron, and E_i is the ionization energy necessary to liberate the electron from its position in the atom. If all the particles are in complete thermal equilibrium at a temperature T, the ratio of the number of ions (A^+) to that of the atoms (A) is given by an expression known as the *Saha equation,* named for the physicist M. N. Saha, who derived it:

$$\frac{(A^+)^2}{(A)^2 - (A^+)^2} = 3.16 \times 10^{-7} \frac{T^{2.5}}{p} \exp\frac{-E_i}{kT}.$$

In the quoted form, the pressure p is in atmospheres, and k is the Boltzmann constant of Eq. 3.25 in Chapter Three. We see that the temperature T, which is in degrees Kelvin, appears in two separate places. The exponential $\dfrac{-E_i}{kT}$ is a function familiar from Chapter Three, and usually appears in equations derived from statistical con-

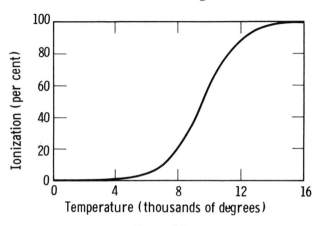

Figure 7.4

siderations. For example, if $E_i = 10^{-11}$ ergs, we obtain the curve shown in Fig. 7.4. As so often the case, the most interesting physical situations take place at either extreme of this curve. When the temperature is relatively low, say at 3000°K, the gas is ionized only weakly. This may occur in flames; for instance, in a welding torch or in the exhaust of a chemical rocket. Under these conditions, the behavior is dominated by the laws of ordinary hydrodynamics, and some interesting practical applications can be realized. One of these is the magnetohydrodynamic or MHD generator, which we will use as an example to illustrate the behavior of weakly ionized plasmas in this temperature region.

In the magnetohydrodynamic generator, electricity is produced by the interaction of a magnetic field with a stream of weakly ionized gas. The principle of such a machine is indicated schematically in Fig. 7.5. From the theory of electricity, it is known that a current is induced in a conductor moving past a magnet. The voltage appears at right angles to the direction of motion and also at right angles to the magnetic field. This is the reason for placing the electrodes as shown. The magnitude of the voltage V depends on the product of the intensity of the magnetic field B, the velocity u with which the plasma moves past the electrodes in the duct, and the distance d between these electrodes. From this product we subtract the ratio of the current density j in the plasma and its conductivity σ. We get

$$V = uBd - j/\sigma.$$

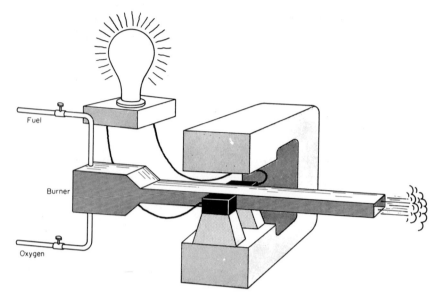

Figure 7.5 Flowing ionized gas

The largest current that such a machine can produce is given by another equation:

$$J_{\max} = uBd\sigma A,$$

in which A is the effective cross-sectional area through which the current can go.

If we examine these equations closely, we note, for instance, that the voltage and the current depend on the dimensions of the machine given in terms of d and A. This is not surprising. It simply means that the larger the generator, the more electricity is produced. The voltage and current also depend on σ, the electrical conductivity. This is somewhat more interesting. σ appears in the denominator of the equation for the voltage in the term $-j/\sigma$. The minus sign in front of it means that high conductivity yields higher and more steady voltages. In the current equation, σ is in the numerator, which means that high conductivity increases the capability of the generator to deliver large currents. In short, high electrical conductivity in the gas stream is desirable for good generator performance. The conductivity, in turn, depends on several factors, especially on the number of ions (A^+) in the plasma. Hence, it is the Saha equation giving the ionization dependence on temperature illustrated in Fig. 7.4 which plays a decisive role in the usefulness of an MHD generator.

Of course, ionization depends not only on the temperature, but also on the pressure p and the ionization energy E_i. In practice, it turns out to be most advantageous to work with a mixture of gases, rather than a single gas. A component with low ionization energy, called *seeding material*, is introduced for the specific purpose of increasing the conductivity. For example, the alkali metals, cesium and potassium, have very low ionization energies. From 0.1 to 2 percent of these substances may be added to the working gas just for the purpose discussed here. The uppermost temperature inside the machine is limited principally by melting or corrosion of the solid materials, which serve as walls of the duct through which the gas flows, and of electrodes through which the electric current flows. An experimental model of an MHD generator is shown in the photograph.

The third observation that should be made regarding the equations for voltage and current concerns the magnetic intensity B and the

(Westinghouse Research Laboratories.)

Experimental model of a 100-kilowatt MHD generator.

velocity u of the plasma stream. These factors appear together and stem from the *Lorentz force,* which is experienced by an electric charge when it is immersed in a magnetic field. In the generator, this force gives rise to a body force, tending to slow down the gas stream, and it is, of course, the origin of the energy that generates electricity.

The Lorentz force has no relation to the temperature of the plasma. Nevertheless, it is going to play an important role in our discussion of high temperature plasmas, because it is a convenient and, ultimately, the only reasonable force available for the manipulation of plasma in the laboratory.

Once a quantity of plasma becomes so hot that it can no longer be left in contact with solid materials, we must look for other means of confining it. In stars, the dominant confining force is gravitation. However, since the magnitude of this attraction is very small, it takes an enormous amount of matter to achieve confinement at such high temperatures. All luminous stars must, therefore, consist of very large masses. Obviously, gravitational force cannot be relied on to confine plasma in the laboratory. Another conceivable way to keep plasma from escaping is to make use of its own inertia. This requires setting up the necessary conditions on a fast enough time scale so that particles in the plasma have no chance to escape before the experiment is completed. This condition is approached in various types of explosions, including nuclear, but of course inertial methods can be utilized only for transient experiments.

The remaining forces at our disposal are of electric and magnetic origin. Electrostatic retarding potentials are often employed to confine and direct streams of electrons or other charged particles. In a thermal plasma, however, where an equal number of positive and negative electric charges exist in any reasonably sized volume, the best that an electrostatic field can do is to separate charges at the surface. It cannot exert any net body force on the material in the volume as a whole.

We are confronted, therefore, with a predicament. In the laboratory we shall have a difficult time trying to confine the plasma, even assuming that otherwise we could produce all the characteristics we desire. The magnetic body force, which we have encountered in the MHD generator, is one of the few forces left to confine the plasma and keep it from dissipation and dilution. In the generator, this force is used to produce electric power, not to confine the plasma, which is done instead by solid walls. But as soon as we begin to deal with plasmas of much higher temperatures, say a million degrees or so, the dominant mode of control for the confinement of plasma becomes the magnetic body force, ultimately based on the Lorentz force.

Laboratory research in temperatures over a million degrees is almost exclusively devoted to the problem of harnessing nuclear fusion for the extraction of useful power. The process of nuclear fusion is a most important natural phenomenon, since it is the agent of energy production both in the sun and in the stars, and consequently also the origin of all the energy on the earth, except nuclear fission. The possibility of using nuclear fusion for power production was actually recognized over a decade before nuclear fission was discovered. The practical difficulty inherent in the realization of controlled fusion—the requirement of extremely high temperatures—is, however, the principal reason why fusion has not yet been harnessed in the laboratory, while fission, which can be sustained at low temperatures, is already put to practical use in many applications.

Let's look at the physics of the fusion process so that the necessity for such high temperatures can be appreciated more fully. The atomic nuclei of all the natural elements can be considered as a conglomeration of protons and neutrons which are held together by strong mutual forces called nuclear forces, whose exact origin is still obscure. Furthermore, because of the intrinsic nuclear spin of the proton and the neutron, and other quantum mechanical properties, certain combinations of these protons and neutrons are particularly stable. This, in itself, is quite analogous to the stability encountered in chemical compounds, and it is possible to produce *nuclear* reactions similar to *chemical* reactions in which more stable products are formed with a release of energy.

Of particular interest to nuclear fusion are two isotopes of hydrogen, *deuterium* and *tritium*, which can be combined to form helium. The following nuclear reactions occur:

$$\text{Deuteron} + \text{Triton} \rightarrow \text{Helium}^4 + \text{Neutron} + \text{Energy}$$
$$\text{Two Deuterons} \longrightarrow \text{Helium}^3 + \text{Neutron} + \text{Energy}$$
$$\text{Two Deuterons} \longrightarrow \text{Triton} \ \ + \text{Proton} \ \ + \text{Energy}$$

All of these reactions liberate large amounts of energy which appear as kinetic energy of the reaction products. In other words, the two particles produced in the reaction fly apart with high speed.

The problem that confronts the scientist working on nuclear fusion is how to bring the primary particles close together, so that they can enter into one of the fusion reactions. The range of the attractive nuclear forces, which are responsible for the reaction, is extremely short. While these forces are very powerful within their domain, they do not extend appreciably beyond the surface of the atomic nucleus itself. It is therefore necessary to bring the two nuclei, which are required for the fusion reaction, into close contact. The distance between them must be less than 10^{-13} cm.

On the other hand, the nuclei, being isotopes of hydrogen, each carry a unit of positive electric charge, and therefore tend to repel each other. The force associated with electric charges is called *Coulomb force*, and this has a relatively long range compared to the nuclear forces. The combination of nuclear and Coulomb forces can be illustrated graphically by the diagram shown in Fig. 7.6, where one of the nuclei is represented as being stationary, while the other nucleus approaches from the right. The repulsing Coulomb force can be pic-

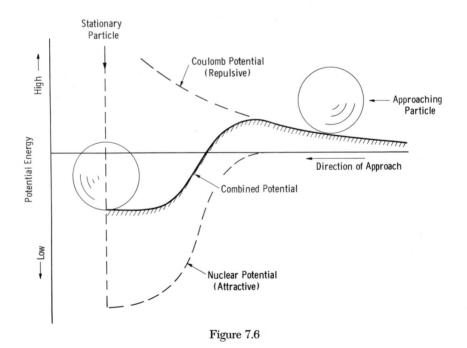

Figure 7.6

tured as a mountain that the approaching nucleus has to climb, while the attracting nuclear force results in a well into which the approaching nucleus falls when it enters into the fusion reaction zone. We can see at once that the two aspects of the Coulomb force, that is, its relatively long range and the fact that it is repulsive, lead to a severe inhibition of nuclear fusion. Two nuclei that approach each other can easily be deflected through a small angle by the Coulomb force long before they get within the range of their respective nuclear forces. Thus, many thousand such glancing collisions occur before two nuclei, by chance, get close enough together so that the attractive nuclear force overcomes the Coulomb repulsion.

For this reason, there is no hope of using an accelerator, such as a cyclotron, as a practical power generator, since if we accelerate deuterons and direct them at a cold stationary target, most of them would lose their energy by Coulomb collisions, and only a very few would succeed in fusion. Such inefficiency can be tolerated in the research laboratory where we intend to do scientific experiments, for which cyclotrons are very useful instruments indeed. But more energy is dissipated this way than is gained back by energy release in fusion. If a positive power output is required, we must somehow preserve the energy lost in Coulomb collisions so that it can be used over and over again, until finally fusion occurs. The only way in which an assembly of particles can be maintained in such a state of internal motion is to be in thermal equilibrium. The distribution of velocities among the particles must have the highest w, in other words, be the most probable, as we learned in Chapter Three. We also learned in the same chapter that any other distribution of velocities—especially at high temperatures—is most unlikely to occur and would require a higher expenditure of energy. In addition, for reasons we need not elaborate on here, other distributions would cause the system to lose energy through radiation at an increased rate; and radiation already represents a considerable loss of power in presently conceivable fusion systems.

Thus, we conclude that the only practical method of nuclear fusion is *thermonuclear* fusion, that is, a plasma in thermal equilibrium. We also note that the nuclear fusion that occurs in the sun and in the stars is of the thermonuclear variety.

From the strength of the Coulomb force and from the particle velocities, we can compute the rate at which fusion will occur at vari-

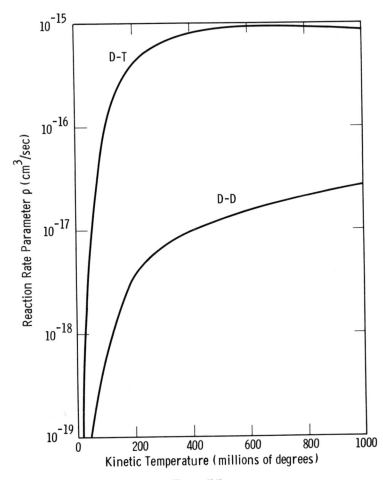

Figure 7.7

ous temperatures in a system. The rate parameter ρ needed for the fusion reactions of the hydrogen isotopes of interest to us on earth is shown in Fig. 7.7. The curves are plotted in highly compressed form, and it can be seen that temperatures of 50 to 200 million degrees are needed to obtain an appreciable effect. The reaction rate R is given by the expression

$$R = n_1 n_2 \rho \text{ reactions/cm}^3/\text{sec},$$

where n_1 and n_2, respectively, stand for the number of reacting particles in a volume of one cubic centimeter.

For example, if we have 10^{15} deuterons per cubic centimeter, which is approximately what one may hope to get, and a like number of tritons, all at a temperature of 200 million degrees, at which

$$\rho = 6 \times 10^{-16},$$

from Fig. 7.7, then we get

$$R = 10^{15} \times 10^{15} \times 6 \times 10^{-16} = 6 \times 10^{14} \text{ reactions/cm}^3/\text{sec}.$$

Each reaction releases 6.8×10^{-13} calories worth of energy, so that the power production would be

$$(6 \times 10^{14}) \times (6.8 \times 10^{-13}) \text{ calories/cm}^3/\text{sec},$$

which is a little over 400 calories of thermal power each second per cubic centimeter of the reacting volume. This is a very high power density for systems to which we are accustomed in the laboratory or in a power plant. We can immediately see, however, several limiting factors in Fig. 7.7. First of all, going to higher temperatures will not gain much more fusion power output, whereas going to lower temperatures, say a reduction to 20 million degrees, will reduce the power by a factor of a thousand, which is serious. Secondly, we cannot hope to obtain such nice results with the reaction of deuterons with deuterons, no matter how hard we try. Even if we were to be satisfied with $\rho = 10^{-17}$, the temperature will have to be over 400 million degrees. Although there is a plentiful supply of deuterium available in ocean water, tritium is not found in nature to any extent and must be manufactured. It can be made from lithium in a fission reactor, but this is not a very good solution to the problem, because fusion power would then be dependent on fission reactors. Tritium can also be made from deuterium by thermonuclear fusion, but of course that presupposes deuterium alone can be made to fuse thermally. Hence, scientists are striving for temperatures of 200 to 1000 million degrees.

It was hinted earlier that, in addition to the requirement of such enormously high temperatures, the particles must be confined and that for all practical purposes magnetic forces alone are available. We need not be afraid that such a hot body would melt any walls with which it might be in contact. The opposite is more likely to occur, that is, the walls would cool the plasma so much that attainment of the required temperatures is prevented.

We need not go into all the intricacies of the problem of magnetic confinement at this point. There are many obstacles that must be overcome. In particular, various types of instabilities are being encountered, which let the plasma escape from the confined volume after a short period of time. Most of these instabilities were discovered only recently, after scientists attempted to produce such hot plasmas in the laboratory. Even if successful methods are found to counteract each one of them, it is not yet known whether or not there are other difficulties unsuspected so far.

We have already mentioned that the length of the confinement achieved to date is in the microsecond and millisecond range. This is not long enough for practical purposes. A successful fusion reactor must confine the plasma at the temperature and pressure we have mentioned for a period approaching or surpassing one second.

Many research laboratories working on thermonuclear fusion are engaged at this time in programs designed to understand more fully the physical behavior of the plasma. Probably the most sophisticated machine in Project Sherwood carries the name: Model C *Stellarator,* a view of which is shown in the photograph. In this device, plasma is confined inside a tube like a *race track,* shaped in the form of an elongated doughnut. The tube's diameter is eight inches, and once around the race track is 40 feet. Several layers of coils surround the tube, producing a very complicated pattern of magnetic lines. Although it is now known that such a machine will never make a practical fusion reactor, it is expected to be a valuable research tool in the study of the strange, and as yet unknown, characteristics of plasmas at millions of degrees of temperature.

NUCLEAR TEMPERATURES

The next big stepping stone on the stairway to high temperatures leads to the fifth state of matter, in which we encounter the nuclear temperatures. Appropriately named for the atomic nuclei, it makes its appearance mainly in nuclear reactions, that is, in the interaction of protons and neutrons with atomic nuclei. In the early part of this chapter, the term nuclear matter was used to denote an assembly of protons and neutrons as they are believed to occur inside an atomic nucleus. Actually, even the largest of the stable nuclei contain only

Model C Stellerator, probably the most sophisticated machine in Project Sherwood. C Stellerator research is being conducted at Princeton University under the sponsorship of the U.S. Atomic Energy Commission.

slightly over 200 such particles, so that we will not be dealing with objects containing 10^{20} particles or more, as has been the case so far, but with only a relatively small number within the boundary of the system. This is getting close to the minimum number for which statistical considerations can be utilized effectively. It has been found experimentally that nuclei having a mass number (mass number = protons + neutrons) of less than 50 do not lend themselves particularly well to statistical treatment, so that the notion of temperature can be applied only to the heavier nuclei.

A typical application of the temperature concept to nuclear reactions can be understood from the following example. An incident particle enters the target nucleus and forms what is known as a *compound nucleus.* By this we mean the condition in which the incident particle remains in the nucleus for a time sufficiently long to lose its identity completely, and share with all the other particles any energy it may have brought in initially. In this way, the excitation energy can be considered as heat energy added to the system. The heating of the compound nucleus then causes evaporation of a particle, usually a neutron. A temperature can be assigned to the residual nucleus after emission, in complete analogy to evaporation of a molecule from a liquid drop.

The situation can be visualized more clearly if we quote some typical numbers. First of all, the example must be chosen so that the compound nucleus is in a region of closely spaced energy levels, from which "evaporation" can occur. For typical medium-heavy nuclei, a minimum of 10 MeV of energy is required. (*MeV* means "million electron volts". This is the kinetic energy acquired by an electron when it is accelerated by a voltage of one million volts. In more usual energy terms, 1 MeV $= 3.83 \times 10^{-14}$ calories, or 4.45×10^{-20} kilowatt-hours.) This minimum energy must be provided either in the form of kinetic energy of the incident particle, using an accelerator such as a cyclotron, or else through a special situation such as fission. Many experimenters in this field use 14 MeV neutrons or 16 MeV protons as incident particles, partly because large fluxes can be obtained by rather standard techniques in electrostatic accelerators and cyclotrons.

Since it takes approximately 10^{-22} second for a particle to travel from one side of a nucleus to the other, we can talk of nuclear heating only when the system has had sufficient time to distribute the additional energy among all of its particles by mutual collisions. This means at least a hundred times, and preferably a thousand or ten thousand times longer than the traversal time. So we see that 10^{-18} second is quite long on a nuclear scale, even though it still seems quite short compared to the time intervals of our everyday experience. It is at this point that evaporation of particles can take place. If neutrons are evaporated, the energy distribution is quite thermal, but for protons a distortion in the energy spectrum becomes apparent, caused by repulsion of the electric charges. Typical energy distributions are shown in Fig. 7.8. From such curves it is possible to infer the tempera-

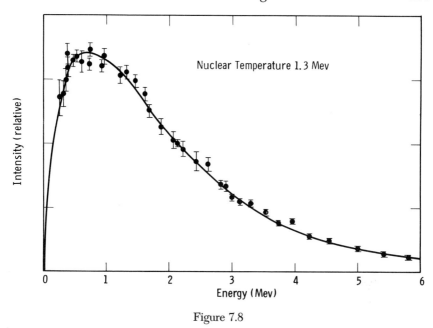

Figure 7.8

ture of the residual nucleus. As we might suspect, this depends on the energy that was originally contributed by the incident particle. Also, it takes more energy to heat up a heavy nucleus than a lighter one. These features are apparent from the data shown in Table 7.A.

In conclusion, we return to the phenomenon of fission for which nuclear temperatures are of great practical importance. Nuclear fission occurs in certain heavy nuclei. When a particle, typically a neutron, is absorbed into one of these heavy nuclei, the resultant compound nucleus is so unstable that it breaks into two or occasionally three

TABLE 7.A

Some Typical Nuclear Temperatures in MeV				
Mass number of nucleus	55	115	181	231
Energy of incident particle				
5	1.6	0.8	0.7	0.6
10	2.2	1.1	1.0	0.9
15	2.7	1.4	1.2	1.1

parts of more or less equal weight. The fission fragments fly apart with high velocities, carrying along most of the liberated energy. Some energy remains, however, inside each fission fragment in the form of nuclear excitation, giving rise to sufficiently high nuclear temperatures so that neutrons can be evaporated. Approximately one neutron with an average energy of one MeV is evaporated from each fission fragment. These neutrons can then be used to initiate additional fission processes, thus setting up the familiar chain reaction which makes possible a sustained fission rate in a nuclear reactor, or a catastrophic increase of the fission rate in an atomic bomb. If it were not for the phenomenon of evaporation of neutrons, self-sustained fission could not exist.

MESON TEMPERATURES

In 1935, the Japanese physicist H. Yukawa showed, by combining two fundamental theories of modern physics—quantum mechanics and the theory of relativity—that a new set of particles should exist, corresponding to the forces that come into play when nuclear particles collide. Since the predicted masses should be between those of electrons and protons, the name *mesons* was suggested. Some ten years later, experimental physicists observed particles, now called *π-mesons,* or *pions,* with the required properties. If, for instance, a very high energy proton collides with a nucleus, a shower of such mesons, as seen in the photograph, may be observed, along with a general breakup of the target nucleus, resulting in a "star." A theoretical analysis has been attempted in which thermal conditions are postulated so that a temperature can be defined. If such a model is valid, that is, if it corresponds to the observed facts, the temperature involved would be the highest yet encountered in nature. The most powerful nuclear accelerators built so far, having accelerating capabilities of 30,000 MeV, are barely able to produce enough mesons in a single collision to warrant statistical treatment. In cosmic rays, however, particles have occasionally been observed with energies greatly in excess of this, and thermal treatment should be valid when such particles collide with a stationary target. Because of the simplicity of the concept of temperature, physicists will undoubtedly

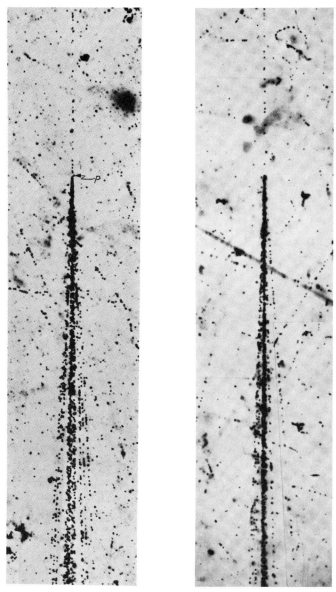

(From "The Study of Elementary Particles by the Photographic Method" by C. F. Powell, P. H. Fowler, and D. H. Perkins. Published by Pergamon Press, New York. Used by permission.)

The collision of a very high energy proton and a nucleus results in a shower of mesons and a general break-up of the target nucleus. The "jets" of mesons shown here were produced by particles of energy ~3000 BeV and ~9000 BeV, respectively.

make every possible effort to check their experimental data for the applicability of a statistical thermodynamic theory.

The velocities of these particles are so high that relativistic corrections must be applied to the calculations. One such theory, developed by Enrico Fermi in the 1950's, is expected to be applicable to particles in excess of ten million MeV.

Perhaps some day machines will be able to produce energies in this range. If so, we may hope to gather sufficient experimental evidence to find out whether it makes sense to talk of "meson temperatures" and the sixth state of matter.

Appendix

Certain Symbols

GREEK ALPHABET

A	α	alpha	I	ι	iota	P	ρ	rho
B	β	beta	K	κ	kappa	Σ	σ	sigma
Γ	γ	gamma	Λ	λ	lambda	T	τ	tau
Δ	δ	delta	M	μ	mu	Υ	υ	upsilon
E	ε	epsilon	N	ν	nu	Φ	φ	phi
Z	ζ	zeta	Ξ	ξ	xi	X	χ	chi
H	η	eta	O	o	omicron	Ψ	ψ	psi
Θ	θ	theta	Π	π	pi	Ω	ω	omega

In scientific notation, it has become customary to use certain symbols, as well as Greek and Roman letters, to denote specific quantities. Throughout this book such symbols have been defined in context, but the following list, intended only for reference, gives commonly accepted definitions of the letters and symbols most frequently encountered.

Δ	finite difference
θ, φ, ψ	angle
φ	work function
λ	wavelength
ν	frequency
ρ	density, or resistivity
ω	angular velocity
c	velocity of light
d	distance
E	energy, or electric field
e	charge of the electron, or the base of the natural logarithms
F	force
f	frequency
G	gravitation constant
g	acceleration of gravity
H	magnetic field intensity
h	Planck's constant
i, I	electric current
k	Boltzmann's constant
l, L	length
m, M	mass
n, N	number, especially an integer
P	pressure
p	momentum
q, Q	amount of charge
R	universal gas constant
r	radius
T	temperature
t	time
v, V	velocity, volume, voltage
∞	infinity

Certain Scientists

ABRAGAM, Anatole (1914–   ). French physicist, professor at Collége de France, noted for his studies of nuclear magnetism and his contributions to solid state physics. Abragam is the author of a recently published book, *The Theory of Nuclear Magnetism.*

AVOGADRO, Count Amadeo (1776–1856). Italian physicist and chemist, who suggested in 1811 the principle that equal volumes of all gases at the same temperature contain identical numbers of molecules. Avogadro's law was much later elucidated by the Maxwell-Boltzmann law of equipartition of energy, and positively established by the experiments of J. J. Thomson, Millikan, Rutherford, and others. Avogadro's Constant is the number of molecules contained in one mole (gram-molecular weight) of a substance.

BLOEMBERGEN, Nicholaas (1920–   ). American scientist, especially known for developing a new type of *maser*, built to operate specifically on the wavelength of interstellar hydrogen. This synthetic ruby crystal device is capable of extending the range of radio telescopes as much as tenfold, making it possible to detect signals from outer space one one-thousandth as strong as those previously observable.

BOLTZMANN, Ludwig (1844–1906). Austrian physicist who is known especially for the Stefan-Boltzmann law of black-body radiation. Boltzmann contributed to the probability theory and the partition of energy in connection with the kinetic theory of gases.

BOSE, Satyendra Nath (1894–   ). Indian physicist. Bose was at Dacca University when he devised a new derivation for Planck's law of radiation; he sent his brief paper to Einstein in 1924. Recognizing the significance of Bose's results and its relation to his own work, Einstein published a German translation which laid the foundation for the new Bose-Einstein statistics.

BRIDGMAN, Percy Williams (1882–1961). American physicist, who was awarded the 1946 Nobel prize in physics for his investigations of various phenomena related to extremely high pressures. Bridgman was a teacher, and the author of a number of books, such as *Dimensional*

Analysis, The Physics of High Pressure, and *The Nature of Thermodynamics.*

CLAPEYRON, B. P. E. (1799–1864). French civil engineer and mathematician. The Clapeyron-Clausius Equation is a fundamental relationship between the temperature at which an interphase transition occurs, the change in heat content, and the change in volume.

COLLINS, Samuel Cornette (1898–   ). American scientist, professor of mechanical engineering at Massachusetts Institute of Technology. Collins has done notable researches in the thermodynamic properties of gases, producing and maintaining very low temperatures, improving oxygen processes of low pressure type.

COULOMB, Charles Augustin de (1736–1806). French physicist, noted for his experiments on friction and for his researches in electricity and magnetism. He formulated Coulomb's law of the forces existing between charged bodies, and the coulomb, a unit of electrical quantity, is named for him.

CURIE, Pierre (1859–1906). French physicist, who discovered the elements radium and polonium, and was also discoverer of the radioactivity of thorium and inducted radioactivity in other elements. Curie also did significant work on piezoelectricity and magnetism. Together with his wife, Marie, he was awarded the Nobel prize in 1903.

DEBYE, Peter Joseph Willem (1884–   ). Dutch physicist, appointed director of the Kaiser Wilhelm Institute in 1935. Debye was awarded the 1936 Nobel prize in chemistry for his notable studies of molecular structure through investigations on dipole moments and on diffraction of x rays and electrons in gases. He is largely responsible for the Debye equation, which connects dielectric constant, dipole moment, and temperature for gases. In 1940 he became head of the Physics Department at Cornell University.

DEWAR, Sir James (1842–1923). Scottish chemist and physicist. Dewar is noted for his investigations of the specific heat of hydrogen, and he was the first to produce liquid hydrogen (in 1899), obtaining it as a solid. He invented the Dewar vessel and also did important work on the properties of matter at low temperatures.

Dirac, P(aul) A(drien) M(aurice) (1902–   ). British mathematical physicist in the field of atomic structure. In 1933 Dirac was awarded the Nobel prize (with Erwin Schrödinger) for his pioneer work in the quantum mechanics of the atom. He was co-discoverer of the Fermi-Dirac statistics, and also pioneered in developing the quantum theory of radiation.

Drude, Paul Karl Ludwig (1863–1906). German physicist, noted for his investigations of the relationship between optical and electrical phenomena, and for his studies of electromagnetic oscillation and the theory of anomalous dispersion.

Dulong, Pierre Louis (1785–1838). French physicist and chemist, discoverer of nitrogen chloride. In 1819, Dulong and Alexis Petit announced the Dulong-Petit law that the product of the specific heat of an element in the solid state, multiplied by its atomic weight, is approximately constant for all elements. Dulong also devised the Dulong formula for calculating the heat value of fuels from their chemical composition.

Einstein, Albert (1879–1955). Mathematician and theoretical physicist, born in Germany. Einstein became a Swiss citizen in his youth, and in 1940 he was naturalized as a citizen of the United States. Each of three papers, published when he was twenty-six, became the source of a new branch of physics. Although Einstein is probably most famous for his theory of relativity, he also did significant work on the photoelectric effect, for which he was awarded the Nobel prize in 1922, as well as on the theory of Brownian movement, emission and absorption of radiation, and particle statistics.

Fermi, Enrico (1901–1954). Italian physicist, who became a United States citizen in 1939. Fermi is noted for his studies in nuclear physics and was awarded the Nobel prize in 1938 for his research on artificial radioactive substances. His investigations have included the quantum theory of radiation, the magnetic movements of nuclei, and the structure of the atom. Fermi was the discoverer of element 93, neptunium, and was one of the leading scientists who contributed to the development of the atomic bomb.

GAUSS, Karl Friedrich (1777–1855). German mathematician, often classed with Newton and Archimedes as one of the three greatest mathematicians of all time. A famous child prodigy, he eventually influenced strongly almost all areas of mathematics, including geometry, number theory, functions of a complex variable, infinite processes, algebra, the theory of errors, physics, and astronomy.

GIAUQUE, William Francis (1895–   ). American chemist, co-discoverer (with Herrick Lee Johnston) of oxygen isotopes. Giauque received the Franklin Institute Elliott Cresson medal for his discovery of the adiabatic demagnetization method of producing temperatures below absolute zero. For his low temperature researches, he was awarded the 1949 Nobel prize in chemistry.

GIBBS, Josiah Willard (1839–1903). American physicist and mathematician, professor of mathematical physics at Yale University from 1871 until his death. His investigations established the basic theory for physical chemistry, and his *Scientific Papers,* published in two volumes in 1906, have proved most fruitful for physicists, chemists, and mathematicians.

JOULE, James Prescott (1818–1889). English physicist, known for his researches in the mechanical equivalent of heat. These studies led to a series of experiments on the equivalence of heat and energy. The joule, a physical unit of work equal to ten million ergs, is named for him. In studying the relations between electrical, mechanical, and chemical effects, Joule discovered the first law of thermodynamics.

KELVIN, Lord (William Thomson) (1824–1907). British physicist, born in Ireland. Kelvin was recognized as one of the greatest physicists of his time. Influenced by Joule's theory of heat, he proposed an absolute scale of temperature independent of any thermometric substance. A few years later, Kelvin reconciled the work of Sadi Carnot with that of Count Rumford, Sir Humphry Davy, J. R. Mayer, and Joule; his resulting dynamical theory of heat and the fundamental principle of conservation of energy commanded universal acceptance. At the same time he first stated briefly his principle of dissipation of energy, the second law of thermodynamics. Kelvin's contributions to thermo-dynamics are considered of primary importance, but he was also responsible for significant advances in many other areas of research.

LORENTZ, Hendrik Antoon (1853–1928). Dutch physicist, whose work was wide in scope but primarily aimed at some consistent theory for electricity, magnetism, and light. However, his "electron theory" failed to explain the negative result of the Michelson-Morley experiment. In his effort to overcome this difficulty, Lorentz extended his work, and finally arrived at the "Lorentz transformation," which formed the basis for the restricted theory of relativity. He was an eager worker in the cause of international science, and in 1902 he was awarded, with Pieter Zeeman, the Nobel prize in physics.

MAXWELL, James Clerk (1831–1879). British physicist, born in Scotland. At the age of fifteen, Maxwell made the first of his many scientific contributions, and by the time he was eighteen his singular genius was becoming apparent. In his extraordinary investigations, which included electricity, magnetism, elastic solids, color perception, and the kinetic theory of gases, Maxwell was not only the experimenter but often the mathematician as well. Of his many great contributions, the most significant dealt with the physical theory of electromagnetism.

MEISSNER, Walther (1882–   ). German physicist, noted for having observed that a pure superconductor, placed in a magnetic field, excludes magnetic induction entirely, and therefore behaves as a perfect diamagnetic whose magnetic permeability is zero. This is known as the "Meissner effect."

NAPIER, John (or Neper) (1550–1617). Scottish mathematician, laird of Merchiston. Napier was the inventor of logarithms, as well as various mechanical computing devices; he was a pioneer in the use of decimal notation.

NYQUIST, H. (1889–   ). American physicist, born in Sweden. As communications engineer at American Telephone and Telegraph Company and Bell Telephone Laboratories, Nyquist made significant contributions to telegraphy. He postulated the theory of thermal agitation of electricity in conductors—the Johnson-Nyquist noise.

ØRSTED, Hans Christian (1777–1851). Danish physicist, especially noted for his discovery of electromagnetism. The oersted, a unit of magnetic field strength in the *emu* system, is named for him.

PETIT, Alexis Therese (1791–1820). French physicist, who with Pierre Dulong developed methods for determining thermal expansion and specific heat of solid bodies. Also with Dulong, he enunciated in 1819 the law of Dulong and Petit, which states that the elements in the solid state have nearly the same atomic heat.

PLANCK, Max (1858–1947). German theoretical physicist, who made the significant discovery that energy exists in quantized form. From this premise, he derived the universal Law of Radiation in 1901. Planck was Professor of Physics at Kiel and at Berlin, and the author of such classic works on theoretical physics as *Theory of Heat Radiation*. He was awarded the 1918 Nobel prize in physics.

SAHA, Meghnad N. (1893–   ). Indian physicist, member of the Indian Scientific Mission to England, the United States, and Canada in 1944–45; president of the National Academy of Sciences of India. Saha is especially noted for his work on radiation and ionization, as well as for his contributions to the theory of spectra.

SOMMERFELD, Arnold (1868–1951). German physicist, noted for his work in atomic physics and radiation. Sommerfeld conducted important researches in quantum theory and the Bohr atomic theory.

THOMSON, William (1824–1907), see *Kelvin*.

TOWNES, C. H. (1915–   ). American physicist, Professor of Physics at Columbia University and Provost at Massachusetts Institute of Technology. Townes is noted for his original concept of the maser principle, and for his pioneer work on masers and lasers.

WEISS, Pierre (1865–1940). French physicist, best known for his work in magnetism and for discovering the molecular unit of magnetic moment, called the *Weiss magneton*.

YUKAWA, Hideki (1907–   ). Japanese physicist, noted for discovering the "meson," a subatomic particle which Yukawa first described in 1933 as smaller than a proton and larger than an electron, "in between matter and energy." In 1948, Yukawa joined the Institute for Advanced Studies at Princeton, New Jersey. He was awarded the 1949 Nobel prize in physics.

ZEEMAN, Pieter (1865–1943). Dutch physicist, who made important researches in optical and electrical science. In particular, Zeeman noted the splitting of lines in the spectrum of a light source when placed in a strong magnetic field. This "Zeeman effect" is important in solar studies. Zeeman shared the 1902 Nobel prize in physics with H. A. Lorentz.

The Authors

Jack Castle, Section Manager of the Physics Department, has been a staff member of the Westinghouse Research Laboratories since 1955. During the past nine years, his research work has included bright display image tubes, the structure of smoke deposits, ferroelectric ceramics, and the paramagnetism of crystals. He has also been active in the development of solid state masers, and recently, in collaboration with associates, he has developed a new type of teaching machine.

Dr. Castle was born and brought up in Buffalo, New York. His undergraduate studies at the University of Buffalo were interrupted by three years in the Army Signal Corp during World War II. In 1947, he graduated magna cum laude, with a Bachelor of Arts degree. Three years later he had received a Ph.D. in physics from Yale University, and he returned to the University of Buffalo for year as an Instructor in the Physics Department. From there he went to Cornell Aero Laboratory, where he was engaged for two years in the development of a Vortex Free Air Thermometer. Returning to the University of Buffalo, where he remained until he joined Westinghouse, he became a Research Associate, primarily concerned with the study of carbons and graphite.

Married while still a college undergraduate, Dr. Castle is now the father of five children, three boys and two girls, ranging in age from one to sixteen years.

WERNER EMMERICH, Manager of Plasma Physics Research and Development, joined the staff of the Westinghouse Research Laboratories in 1952. After first developing an efficient fast neutron detector, he then turned to theoretical work in nuclear physics, assisting in the development of the optical model. In 1958, he became interested in nuclear fusion and the physics of ionized gases. He developed the first combustion-fired magnetohydrodynamic generator, and he holds a basic patent on electric arc chambers for supersonic wind tunnel application.

Dr. Emmerich was born in Germany and completed his high school education there before coming to this country in 1937. He was first employed by the Frank Tea and Spice Company in Cincinnati, Ohio, as a salesman, but he much preferred to spend his time in their laboratory and succeeded in developing the formula for the product now marketed as "Mister Mustard." After spending the war years as an interpreter in the U.S. Army, he entered Ohio State University, graduating cum laude in 1949 with a B.S. degree. He stayed on at the University for graduate studies, receiving a Ph.D. in physics.

Dr. Emmerich is married and has three young children, a daughter and two sons. His wife shares his enthusiasm for skiing, which is one of his favorite forms of relaxation. He is a member of Phi Beta Kappa, Sigma Xi, and the American Physical Society, and has contributed to a number of books, both scientific and educational.

ROBERT HEIKES, Director, Solid State Science Research and Development, had just completed his graduate work in physics at the University of Chicago and received his Ph.D. degree, when he joined the staff of the Westinghouse Research Laboratories in 1952.

Brought up in Harrisburg, Pennsylvania, he had the benefit of some stimulating instructors in his scientific and mathematical high school courses. He soon decided on a scientific career, studying first at the Massachusetts Institute of Technology and graduating with a Bachelor of Science degree.

Dr. Heikes was married the same year he came to Westinghouse, and he is now the father of a nine-year-old daughter. In recent years he has formed the enjoyable habit of a working-vacation at CNRS, a scientific laboratory in Paris. Here he is not only able to participate in the scientific activities of another laboratory, but is also able to further two of his greatest loves: the study of foreign languages and the consumption of French food and wine. In fact, Dr. Heikes and his wife take great pride in preparing gourmet dinners for their friends. On these occasions individually styled menus, enhanced by original French verse, are usually prepared.

ROBERT MILLER, Section Manager of the Department of Solid State Phenomena, has been on the staff of the Westinghouse Research Laboratories since 1956.

A native Pennsylvanian, he was born in the town of Perkasie, and received his early education there. While still in grade school, he started building radios and other electronic devices with his father. He says that once his interest was aroused, he "sort of drifted into science." After graduating with a Bachelor of Science degree in chemistry from Juniata College in Huntingdon, Pennsylvania, he was engaged by Mellon Institute in Pittsburgh to work on gas reactions. A year later, he went on to Yale University for graduate studies in physical chemistry.

In 1952, with a Ph.D. from Yale, he joined the staff of the Chemistry Department at Princeton University, and for several years did research work on the dielectric constant of liquids.

Four years after joining the Westinghouse Research staff, Dr. Miller married the vivacious secretary of the Chemistry Department. The Millers, who now have two small girls, share many interests and hobbies. They are both amateur geologists, and spend vacations tramping remote hillsides with pick and shovel, adding to their collection of rock specimens. Dr. Miller also builds cannons in his spare time, and is an authoritative and avid collector of antique single-shot target rifles and cartridges.

JOHN RAYNE became a member of the Westinghouse Research Laboratories' staff in 1956, and since then has worked in the areas of low temperature physics and the physics of metals.

Born and brought up in Sydney, Australia, he attended elementary and high school there, and then went on for undergraduate college studies in science and engineering at the University of Sydney, graduating with B.S. and B.E. degrees. As long as he can remember, he had wanted to be an engineer, and he now started work as an electrical engineer in a power station. It took only six months for him to decide that he was more interested in physics.

When he was awarded a Fulbright-Hays scholarship, he came to this country for graduate studies at the University of Chicago, receiving a Ph.D. in physics in 1954. With his American bride, he returned to Australia, and for the next two years worked on the research staff of the Low Temperature Laboratory of Commonwealth Scientific and Industrial Research Organization in Sydney.

In addition to his research work, Dr. Rayne teaches in the Physics Department of Carnegie Institute of Technology, and still finds time to devote to his family. The Raynes now have three children, two girls and a boy.

For Further Reading

Part One

Bowden, Sydney T. *The Phase Rule and Phase Reactions: Theoretical and Practical.* New York: St. Martin's Press, Inc., 1954.

Daniels, Farrington, and Alberty, Robert A. *Physical Chemistry.* 2nd ed. New York: John Wiley & Sons, Inc., 1961.

Davison, Albert W.; Van Klooster, Henry S.; Bauer, Walter H., and Janz, George J. *Laboratory Manual of Physical Chemistry.* 4th ed. New York: John Wiley & Sons, Inc., 1956.

Findlay, Alexander, (Campbell, A. N., and Smith, N. O.) *The Phase Rule and its Applications.* 9th ed. New York: Dover Publications, Inc., 1951.

Glasstone, Samuel, and Lewis, David. *Elements of Physical Chemistry.* 2nd ed. Princeton, New Jersey: D. Van Nostrand Co., Inc., 1960.

Glasstone, Samuel. *Textbook of Physical Chemistry.* 2nd ed. Princeton, New Jersey: D. Van Nostrand Co., Inc., 1946.

Partington, J. R. *An Advanced Treatise on Physical Chemistry;* Vol. I: *Fundamental Principles and the Properties of Gases.* 1949. Vol. II: *The Properties of Liquids.* 1951. Vol. III: *The Properties of Solids.* 1952. New York: John Wiley & Sons, Inc., 1949, 1951, 1952.

Reilly, Joseph, and Rae, William Norman. *Physico-Chemical Methods,* Vol. I. Princeton, New Jersey: D. Van Nostrand Co., Inc., 1954.

Taylor, Hugh S., and Glasstone, Samuel. *Treatise on Physical Chemistry, Vol. II: States of Matter.* Princeton, New Jersey: D. Van Nostrand Co., Inc., 1951.

Part Two

Abragam, A. *The Principles of Nuclear Magnetism.* Oxford: The Clarendon Press, 1961.

Bohr, Niels Henrik David. *Atomic Physics and Human Knowledge.* New York: John Wiley & Sons, Inc., 1958.

Gurney, Ronald Wilfrid. *Introduction to Statistical Mechanics.* 1st ed. New York: McGraw-Hill Book Co., 1949.

Pake, George Edward. *Paramagnetic Resonance, An Introductory Monograph.* New York: W. A. Benjamin, 1962.

Planck, Max K. *Treatise on Thermodynamics.* 3rd ed. New York: Longmans, Green & Co., Inc., 1927.

Slichter, Charles P. *Principles of Magnetic Resonance (with examples from solid state physics).* New York: Harper & Row, 1963.

Troup, Gordon. *Masers; Microwave Amplification and Oscillation by Stimulated Emission.* New York: John Wiley & Sons, Inc., 1959.

Teachers' references:

Sommerfeld, Arnold Johannes Wilhelm. *Atomic Structure and Spectral Lines.* trans. from 3rd German ed. New York: E. P. Dutton & Co., Inc., 1923.

Townes, Charles H., and Schawlow, A. L. *Microwave Spectroscopy.* New York: McGraw-Hill Book Co., 1955.

Part Three

Bishop, Amasa S. *Project Sherwood; the U. S. Program in Controlled Fusion.* Reading, Mass.: Addison-Wesley Publishing Co., 1958.

Hoare, Frank E.; Jackson, L. C.; and Kurti, N. eds. *Experimental Cryophysics.* London: Butterworth, 1961.

Jackson, Leonard C. *Low Temperature Physics.* New York: John Wiley & Sons, Inc., 1955.

MacDonald, David Keith Chalmers. *Near Zero: An Introduction to Low Temperature Physics.* Garden City, New York: Doubleday & Co., Inc., (Anchor Books), 1961.

Mendelsohn, Kurt. *Cryophysics.* New York: (Interscience) John Wiley & Sons, Inc., 1960.

Shoenberg, David. *Superconductivity.* 2nd ed. Cambridge: The University Press, 1938.

Ulman, Martin A. *Introduction to Plasma Physics.* New York: McGraw-Hill Book Co., 1964.

Index